Great
Historical
Blunders

Great Historical Blunders:

Mistakes That Changed the Course of Science, Technology and History

PERE ROMANILLOS

KONECKY&KONECKY

Konecky & Konecky
72 Ayers Point Road
Old Saybrook, CT 06475

Original Title

GRANDES ERRORES DE LA HUMANIDAD
© 2010, Pere Romanillos
© 2010, Editorial Océano, S.L.
Grupo Océano - Barcelona, Spain

Translated by Sean Konecky
English text copyright © Konecky & Konecky, 2016

ISBN: 978-1-56862-816-8

DREAMSTIME

WIKIPEDIA COMMONS

22 ©Marie-Lan Nguyen; 24 BY DieBuche; 47 BY James Steakley; 127 BY Paravis; 149 wiki BY

Josep Renalias; 179 BY David Monniau; 204b BY xantener; 213a BY AgnosticPreachersKid; 215 BY

Yann; 216 BY Pete Souza, The Obama-Biden Transition Project; 233 BY Lyn Gateley; 238 BY ignis;

242 BY Calibas; 252a BY d-online; 265 BY

Anynobody; 269a BY Jolomo at en.wikipedia; 269b BY Simone.lippi at it.wikipedia; 271 BY Obi

from Roma; 276 ©Elena Filatova; 277a BY Lamiot on fr.wikipedia

GETTY

85

Printed in Korea

Two things are infinite: the universe and human stupidity; and I'm not sure about the universe.

Albert Einstein

contents

Introduction 9

History

A Bite of the Apple 14

The Trojan Horse 20

Baby, It's Cold Outside 26

Love Can Be Deadly 32

Don't Go into the Office Today, Dear 38

Greenland. Not Very Green 44

The End Is Near (Again) 48

Leaning Tower of Pisa 54

Welcome to Japan 58

The Gods Have Landed 64

Bewitched 70

Is London Burning? 76

I Need a Drink 82

Hitler: Recipient of Nobel Peace Prize? 88

The Great Leap Forward 94

Science and medicine

The Earth Is Flat 100

Who Says I'm Not the Center of the Universe 106

A Sense of Humors 114

This May Hurt a Little (I) 120

A Snort a Day 126

Thank You for Smoking 130

This May Hurt a Little (II) 134

The Tragedy of Thalidomide 138

Operation Ranch Hand 142

With a Little Bit of Luck 146

War is Hell

A Superstitious General 154

Russia? Not a Problem 158

Waterloo 162

One for the Indians 166

Botched Landing at Gallipoli 172

Fighting the Last War 176

Back to Russia 180

Could the Day of Infamy Have Been Avoided 186

Business

Black Thursday **194**

The Beatles? Never Heard of Them **198**

Olympic Debacle in Montreal **202**

ET Doesn't Like M&Ms **206**

It Seemed Like a Good Idea **208**

Subprime Meltdown **212**

Technology

What Could Go Wrong? **220**

Man the Lifeboats! **226**

For Want of a Hyphen **234**

Tacoma Bridge Is

Falling down **240**

Environment

Look at the Pretty Bunny **246**

How to Destroy an Island **250**

The Day the Big Wave Hit **254**

To err is human

Port or Starboard? **260**

Not Ready for Takeoff **264**

Midnight in Bhopal **268**

This Is Just a Test **272**

The Challenger Disaster **278**

Fatal Errors 285

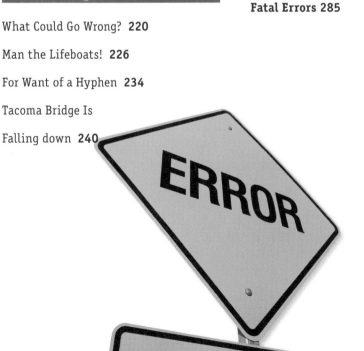

Introduction

In an era of information technology, the great ally of any writer (apart from the internet and rebrewed coffee) is the magic combination of two keys: Ctrl + Z. This simple gesture allows us to undo the last operation and avoid some unprintable mess. Too bad there is not this kind of cyber deletion in real life. It would save us from many blunders. Because, let's face it, no one is infallible. The history of humanity is full of mistaken ideas on which are based bad, bad decisions. The earth is flat; if I sail west I'll get to India; this luxury liner is unsinkable; my army will conquer Russia in three months. . . History has repeatedly shown that our stupidity can lead to ever more serious failures: wars, diseases, pests, accidents, disasters and global crises that could have been avoided with a little more prudence and common sense. If experience is a mountain we climb, one would think that we can learn from our stumbles. But just a quick look at history shows that again and again we trip over the same obstacles. Whether by pure bad luck, misinformation or a deplorable lack of preparation, many of the historical errors that appear in this book have had disastrous consequences. Since the expulsion from the Garden of Eden for eating the forbidden fruit, humankind has amassed a vast assortment of blunders. Slips and falls that have cost the lives of hundreds or thousands of people, poor decisions that have brought about the fall of empires, displays of ignorance that have undermined the economies of entire countries. . .

CTRL + Z: A simple step allows us to void the last completed action and start with a clean slate.

But if we take a look at history we see that we are continually tripping over the same bump in the road.

Madmen or Visionaries?

Everyone screws up at one time or another. Reason plays tricks on us concealing the fatal flaw in something we think is a master plan. Hannibal must have had that

The fire of faith burned in the Middle Ages. So did witches and heretics.

idea when he insisted on crossing the Alps with an army of 60,000 men, 8,000 horses and 50 elephants; Napoleon and Hitler, when they decided to march on Russia, or Columbus, when he landed in the Americas convinced that he was in Japan. Today, they all look crazy, but at the time they were completely convinced of the rightness of what they had accomplished. For Anaximander, the earth was a cylinder; Ptolemy put us in the center of the universe; the Pisan architect thought his plans for a tower were wholly adequate; Custer was sure of victory; New Coke was going to become a bestseller; the French generals rested safe and secure behind the Maginot Line. . . It is also true that sometimes, circumstances, environment or the historical moment don't help things. It is easy to laugh now at Greek astronomers or the great explorers, but hindsight is 20/20 and we look back with all the advantages of our advanced technology. When we have to choose between a plan A and a plan B, many factors come into play: big mistakes have been caused by moments of anger, envy, greed, faith, pride, lust, sloth or unrequited love. Eve, seduced into disobedience, exiled us from Paradise; Caesar's pride led him to the floor of the Roman senate on the Ides of March; warped beliefs fanned the flames of medieval witch hunts; Hitler's overweening egotism made him fail in Russia... Seen in perspective, it seems simple to avoid most of these mistakes. History, however, is not only the story of great human achievements, but also of bobbles, fumbles and just plain stupidity.

Contents of this book

The book is divided into eight chapters: History; Science and Medicine; Warfare; Business; Technology; Environment; To Err Is Human; and Fatal Errors. A long list of blunders explained in a simple and direct tone. We invite you to stroll through errors, mistakes and bad decisions, their protagonists and the changes that resulted from them. The list does not pretend to be exhaustive. No question, humanity will continue making mistakes, but at least we can look at the ones we have already made. And, as the philosopher and essayist George Santayana said, "Those who do not remember the past are condemned to repeat it."

To avoid making blunders NASA has reduced space travel. A couple of broken shuttles and the budgetary concerns have temporarily grounded the space adventure. **Above:** Image from *A Trip to the Moon* a 1902 movie by Georges Méliès.

HISTORY

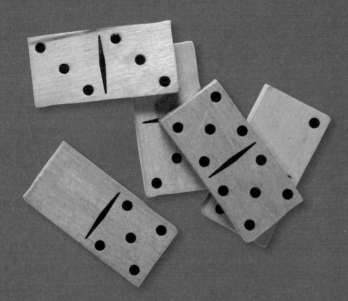

A Bite of the Apple

ERROR: Eating the Forbidden Fruit.

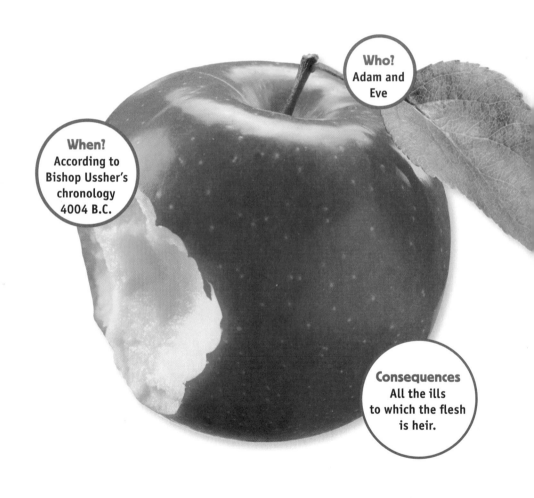

Who?
Adam and
Eve

When?
According to
Bishop Ussher's
chronology
4004 B.C.

Consequences
All the ills
to which the flesh
is heir.

According to Jewish, Christian and Islamic tradition, Adam and Eve were the first people to live on earth. Their only obligation was to grow and reproduce in the Garden of Eden, a paradise that was a real bargain. Eternally vacationing in a five-star hotel, surrounded by nature, free from sickness and, best of all, no work! Who could ask for more? The Creator insisted, however, on one small and insignificant condition: they were not to eat the forbidden fruit of the so-called "tree of knowledge of good and evil." Doing so would lead to their expulsion from paradise. It would seem easy to obey something as simple as that, but according to religious tradition, the devil disguised as a serpent (identified as Satan or Shaitan, "the tempter") took advantage of human weakness to persuade Eve to disobey the Lord. And to think she could get away with it. Our primal mother was deceived, and, not content to enjoy the fruit on her own, she convinced Adam to join her. God immediately carried out his threat. He punished mankind, driving us out of paradise, and slammed the door behind us leaving us with death, pain, shame and labor (which, by the way, led to civilization). God tells Adam: "In the sweat of your face you shall eat bread/Till you return to the ground, / For out of it you were taken; / For dust you are, / And to dust you shall return." (Genesis 3: 19) and tells Eve "in pain you shall bring forth children." (Genesis 3: 16). This blunder is known as "original sin" in the three Abrahamic religions, each interprets this very differently. While the Bible places the blame on Eve for allowing herself to be tempted, according to the Koran both shared in the guilt and were justly punished by exile. Islam does not condemn human nature as such and also explicitly rejects the idea that someone should pay for the mistakes of others: "No bearer of burdens will bear the

Eve offers Adam the apple and he falls for it. Who can resist temptation? Like poorly educated children, the first couple could not obey their creator and ate of the Tree of the Knowledge of Good and Evil. And so here we are.

burden of another." (Sura 17, verse 15)

What Science Tells Us

The scientific viewpoint differs from that of Scripture in many respects. In one regard, however, both are similar. Science also asserts that humanity has common evolutionary ancestors, one male and one female, named after their Biblical counterparts. The scientific Eve is known as mitochondrial Eve, an African woman who possessed the mitochondria of the current human population. That is, the mitochondrial Eve alone produced a continuous line of daughters until our times; therefore, she is the female ancestor from whom all the current population descends. But what is that mitochondria? Cellular elements that are only passed from the mother to the children. According to genetic theory, modern humans (Homo sapiens) originated in Africa between 100,000 and 200,000 years ago. Scientists also refer to the chromosomal Adam. Just as mitochondria are maternally inherited, so are chromosomes inherited from the father. Thus, we all have the same original father.

The forbidden fruit

But to return to the fruit that caused all of this strife. Popular belief identifies it as an apple. This, however, is mistaken. The Bible never specifies what kind of fruit the Tree of the Knowledge of Good and Evil bore. It tells us: "So when the woman saw that the tree was good for food, that it was pleasant to the eyes, and a tree desirable to make one wise, she took of its fruit and ate. She also gave to her husband with her, and he ate." (Genesis 3:6) Not a word about "apples."

This misconception arose during the Middle Ages. The words for "evil" and "apple" are the same in Latin: malum.

A strange-looking snake with the body of a woman emerges from the stone facade of Notre Dame, doubly implicating women for all the sins the flesh is heir to..

At what point in man's evolution did he decide to disobey and reach up for the fruit of the tree of knowledge?

In addition, the apple is one of the first fruits to be cultivated in Asia Minor, dating to at least as early as 1200 B.C. Among the possible candidates for the forbidden fruit, Biblical scholars consider the fig most likely. They rely on the fact that once having eaten the fruit, Adam and Eve realized they were naked and covered themselves with leaves from the same tree from which they had taken the fruit. Many medieval miniatures depict Eve and Adam taking the fruit of a fig tree. Hebrew scholars incline toward the pomegranate, which is often mentioned in the Hebrew Bible. This round fruit, with its red leathery skin, and rich in edible seeds, was being cultivated in Egypt since before the time of Moses.

Fig or apple? It is likely that the Tree of Knowledge of Good and Evil was a fig rather than an apple tree, and its leaves were used to make the first garments.

When did this happen?

In the seventeenth century, the Anglican Archbishop James Ussher (1581–1656) had the temerity to put a date to the birth of humanity. According to his famous chronology (*Annales veteris testamenti, a prima mundi origine mundi deducti*, "Annals of the Old Testament, derived from the beginnings of the world") the first day of creation began on the evening before Sunday 23, October 4004 B.C. of the Julian calendar. How was he able to come up with this date? At that time, it was believed that life on earth would exist for 6,000 years. (4,000 years before the birth of Christ and 2,000 years thereafter). Following a suggestion by the German astronomer Johannes Kepler (1571–1630), Ussher linked the crucifixion of Jesus, during which the sky grew dark, with a solar eclipse that astronomers of the time had identified. Starting with this date his calculation delayed the date of creation four years, fixing the date of 4004 b.c. According to these calculations, the end of the world was to occur in 1997. Fortunately, he missed the mark

here. Ussher also set dates for other important Biblical episodes. Here are the most famous:

- 4004 b.c.: Creation
- 2348 b.c.: The Flood
- 1491 b.c.: The Exodus from Egypt.

Ussher's treatise gained widespread acceptance among the leading European scientific and religious thinkers of the time and ended up appearing as a chronology printed in the margins of the Bible itself. It remained there until well into the nineteenth century.

Bishop James Ussher calculated that the world began on October 23, 4004 B.C.

The Greek version

Many cultures have stories of a primal mistake. Greek mythology tells the famous story of Pandora, an alter ego of Eve or the first human woman, but with more complex and even lurid touches. According to myth, men lived like kings during the Golden Age. They were immortal, and neither worked or grew old. They did not, however, possess wisdom. They were foolish but happy, living securely under the protection of the gods. Everything was under control until Prometheus stole fire from the gods and gave it to men, thus giving them wisdom. This theft angered Zeus. As punishment he sent mankind the irresistibly beautiful Pandora who brought with her a mysterious jar ("Pandora's box" is a mistranslation dating from the Renaissance). It contained all the world's ills:

Where was Eden?

According to the Bible, Eden was a garden situated in the east, in what today is considered the Middle East.

Four rivers ran through Eden dividing it into quarters: Pison (which surrounded the land of Havilah); Gihon (encompassing the land of Cush, that is Ethiopia); and the rivers Tigris and Euphrates. The geography here seems a bit askew. In any event the actual location of the garden is not known; it might have been in Iraq, Jordan, Turkey or Armenia in the vicinity of Mt. Ararat.

After a few generations, God sent the Flood that wiped out all of mankind except for Noah and his family. It also washed away all traces of Eden. All that is known for certain is the facts recorded in Genesis, although it has over the course of time been thought that it was located at Mt. Safon near Hebron (referred to in Isaiah) or even in Jerusalem itself.

envy, hatred, greed, poverty. . . and death. What a gift! To make things even worse, Zeus asked the god Hermes to add in falsehood, lies and an insatiable curiosity. Before being sent down to men, Pandora was warned that she should not under any circumstances open the jar. But like Eve, she could not resist temptation. She opened the gift, and all its many evils flew out. Pandora resealed the container, but it was too late: inside, only hope remained.

Prometheus bound.

The previous page shows a sculptural rendering of the Greek hero who brought fire, symbolizing knowledge, to humanity. For bestowing this godlike gift on mortals, Zeus punished him by chaining him to a rock where a vulture perpetually fed on his liver.

The Trojan Horse

ERROR: Taking a wooden horse filled with enemies armed to the teeth into the walls of Troy.

Who?
The Trojans

When?
About 1200 B.C.

Consequences
The destruction of Troy at the hands of the Greeks

And now the Argive squadron was sailing in order from Tenedos, and in the favoring stillness of the quiet moon sought the shores it knew; when the royal galley ran out a flame, and, protected by the gods' malign decrees, Sinon stealthily lets loose the imprisoned Grecians from their barriers of pine; the horse opens and restores them to the air; and joyfully issuing from the hollow wood, Thessander and Sthenelus the captains, and terrible Ulysses, slide down the dangling rope, They sweep down the city buried in drunken sleep; the watchmen are cut down, and at the open gates they welcome all their comrades, and unite their confederate bands.

Virgil, *The Aeneid*

Who would accept a gift from his most feared enemy and take it into his home? This happened in the famous Trojan War, at the beginning of the twelfth century b.c., although it is not clear whether what we know of the Trojan War is simply a legend or if the conflict actually happened. Most of our knowledge comes from the epic poems *The Iliad* and *The Odyssey*, which are attributed to Homer. There is also a graphic description of the Fall of Troy in Virgil's *Aeneid*. According to Homer the Greeks set out on a punitive expedition. The casus belli was the abduction of Helen of Sparta, wife of King Menelaus, at the hands of Paris son of Priam, the king of Troy. Legendary material aside, the reality is that Troy enjoyed a strategic commercial position much envied by the Greeks. The city overlooked the

The abduction of Helen by Paris, son of the Trojan king, Priam, brought about the Trojan War and the eventual destruction of the city.

Dardanelles Strait, which links the Mediterranean Sea with the Black Sea and the coast of Asia Minor. This location allowed it to monopolize trade, posing a major obstacle to the Mycenaean expansion. Accordingly, it has been argued that the siege of Troy occurred because of economic rather than sentimental reasons.

The abduction of Helen

But back to the myth that forms the basis of the first great epic poetry. According to Homer, the forces that would eventually lead to war were set in motion at the wedding of King Peleus and the Goddess Thetis. To celebrate their nuptials, they invited all the gods except Eris, the goddess of discord. In response she sent a golden apple (the famous apple of discord) to the banquet inscribed with the phrase "to be awarded to the most beautiful." The goddesses Hera, Athena and Aphrodite each maintained that she deserved the title. To resolve their quarrel Zeus allotted to young Paris the task of choosing the winner. Each of the goddesses promised him the gift that lay within her power. Hera promised him power, Athena wisdom, and Aphrodite, the most beautiful woman in the world. Paris decided on Aphrodite. The goddess took the boy to Sparta, where she presented him to Helen, wife of King Menelaus. Taking advantage of the king's absence, Paris kidnapped the beautiful queen abducting her to Troy. Upon his return, the Spartan king and his brother Agamemnon,

Aphrodite, the goddess of love, won the competition for the golden apple by offering Paris the gift of the most beautiful woman in the world.

The Trojan Horse was made of wood. Within its belly was concealed a troop of Greek soldiers, who opened the gates once the horse was taken into the city.

king of Mycenae, summoned all the Greek kingdoms and launched the Trojan war. Led by Agamemnon, 15,000 warriors aboard 300 ships left the port of Aulida to lay siege to Troy.

Achilles avenged the death of his close friend Patroclus on the field of battle by killing Hector in single combat.

Guile rather than force

Because of their vast numbers, the Greeks thought that they would make short work of the invasion. Much to their chagrin, bitter war before the walls of the city lasted for ten years. Finally, the Greeks came up with one last stratagem. Odysseus, king of Ithaca, proposed building a large, hollow wooden horse, constructed to hide a number of soldiers within it. The rest of the army pretended to sail away leaving the horse as a peace offering and a gift to the Gods. The

Agamemnon was the leader of the Greek army. His name means "stubborn." He was the brother of Menelaus, the abduction of whose wife, Helen, led to the Greek attack.

famous contraption was built by Epeüs, the Greeks' most gifted carpenter. The Greek fleet left Troy, only to conceal itself behind an island off the coast. The horse bore the words: "In hopes of a safe return home after an absence of ten years the Greeks dedicate this offering to Athena." The Trojans fell for the trick. The Greek priest Sinon, pretending to have gone over to the Trojan side, convinced them to introduce the horse into the city. The horse was of such size that they had to demolish part of the walls to bring it into the city. Once inside the impregnable fortress, the Greeks left their hiding place and opened the gates of the city, allowing entry to the rest of the troops. The city was plundered mercilessly and burnt to the ground. Menelaus recovered Helen and returned with her to Sparta. According to Virgil a few Trojans escaped. Led by Aeneas they sailed first to Carthage and then to Italy, where they became the ancestors of the founders of Rome.

A remarkable discovery

The beautiful but unlikely story of the Trojan War gained credence when a rich Prussian, Heinrich Schliemann, invested much of his fortune to discover the lost city of Troy. This happened in 1870, when a team of archaeologists led by Schliemann began digging in Hissarlik, a hill located on the edge of a headland projecting into the Aegean between the Dardanelles and the Gulf of Edremit (Turkey). This mound was an artificial mountain formed over the course of centuries by settlements of different peoples, including the Trojans. Under tons of dirt and debris, a total of ten different cities came to light. Of these, it is believed that the so-called Trojan VII is the authentic Ilium of Homer. Among the remains found in this stratum were skeletal remains, weapons, deposits of gravel (that might have been slingshot ammunition) and the grave of

a girl covered with a number of vessels with provisions, indicating a hasty burial possibly because of the siege. The ruins found match Homer's description, if we grant the poet artistic exaggeration in describing luxurious palaces, since Troy was actually a fortress containing a city within its high gates. In 1998, the archaeological site of Troy was declared a World Heritage Site by UNESCO, which stated: "The Archaeological Site of Troy has 4,000 years of history. Its extensive remains are the most significant and sub-stantial evidence of the first contact between the civilizations of Anatolia and the burgeoning Mediterranean world. Excavations started more than a century ago have established a chronology that is fundamental to the understanding of this seminal period of the Old World and its cultural development. Moreover, the siege of Troy by Mycenaean warriors from Greece in the 13th century B.C., immortalized by Homer in The Iliad, has inspired great artists throughout the world ever since."

Baby, It's Cold Outside

ERROR: Crossing the Alps on foot and exposing his men to extreme weather conditions.

Who?
Hannibal Barca (Born in Carthage died in Bithynia on the coast of the Black Sea).

When?
October of 218 B.C.

Consequences
The death of 40,000 men and the weakening of an army that eventually succumbed to Rome at the Battle of Zama.

Once [Hannibal] reached Italy, he made camp right at the foot of the Alps, and let his troops recover for a while. His entire force had not only been exhausted by the ascent and descent, and the harsh conditions on the trail, but were also suffering badly from lack of food and neglect of their bodily needs. In fact, many had completely succumbed to hunger and the constant hardship. The ruggedness of the terrain had made it impossible for them to transport enough food for so many thousands of men, and then most of what they had been carrying had been lost along with the pack animals.

In this cartoon from 1850, a child Hannibal swears eternal hatred towards the Romans. As an adult, he led his troops on a wild ride through the Alps to defeat the Romans in battle.

Polybius, *History of the Roman Republic*

It took over one hundred years for Rome to defeat its rival Carthage and gain undisputed control over the Mediterranean Sea. Rome and Carthage (whose defunct empire was centered in present-day Tunisia) spent more

than a century battling each other in the famous Punic Wars (from 264 B.C. to 146 B.C.). It all began with Rome's annexation of Greece, which did not please the Carthaginians. Carthage at this time dominated the western Mediterranean maritime trade and did not want to lose its business empire. They looked with suspicion at Roman expansionism. The First Punic War (264–241 B.C.) was a walk in the park for the Roman military. It crushed the Carthaginian armies in most battles. It ended with the signing of a peace treaty in which Carthage gave Rome complete control of the strategic island of Sicily. The Carthaginians then devoted their efforts to expanding their colonial empire in Hispania (present-day Spain and Portugal). All went smoothly until 219 B.C., when the Carthaginian general Hannibal attacked the town of Sagunto, which was allied to Rome. Thus began the Second Punic War.

A Roman soldier with spear and shield.

More difficult still

After several battles, the Carthaginian general had enough of fighting on his own territory and decided to attempt something no one had yet dared to try: attack Rome on its home ground. The fastest way to get there was by sea (from Sagunto), but since the defeat of the First Punic War, the Roman navy dominated the Mediterranean. So Hannibal decided to try something even harder. Unable to move his troops by sea, he chose to go by land, traveling over 1,500 miles across the Pyrenees and the Alps. Considered one of the most remarkable military feats in history, Hannibal brought together 60,000 men (mostly soldiers of Iberian origin, along with African, Celtic and Greek mercenaries), 8,000 horses and 50 elephants with which he left New Carthage (now Cartagena, Spain) in May 218 B.C., heading north. By the time he reached the Pyrenees, 7,000 men had deserted owing to the difficulties and risks of the expedition. But worse was to come. The first serious obstacle encountered was crossing the Rhone River with his lumbering elephants. Hannibal had large earth-covered rafts built and drove the animals onto them on wooden planks also covered with earth so that the elephants did not take fright. Bringing elephants along seemed like a good idea at the time. During the march they were very helpful, as they were able to carry ten times more weight than a horse; they were also a powerful fighting force: they could carry assault turrets and enemy troops were terrorized by their mere presence. However, Hannibal did not fully account for the rigors of the journey and the toll it would take.

An African in the snow

The expedition set off at a good pace thanks in part to the negotiations and agreements that the general's emissaries had previously established with the tribes whose territories they were to cross. The main column moved along the Rhone valley to the vicinity of Valence. From there, they turned eastward and in late October, arrived at the confluence of the Rhone and the Isère, at the foot of the fearsome Alps. The Carthaginian general wanted to get across the mountains before winter. But the expedition was delayed and the army had to confront steep and dangerous peaks under conditions for which they were entirely unprepared. (Picture an African of the third century B.C. on foot crossing peaks 10,000 feet high in freezing temperatures accompanied by some animals that had never seen snow.) Hannibal wanted to attack

Elephants, brought from the savannahs of Africa, had to deal with cold mountain passes and lack of food.

Rome by surprise and needed to cross the mountains as quickly as possible. But these were not mere hills but large peaks with high snow-covered passes The Carthaginian general went on until the extreme conditions and several avalanches took the lives of some 40,000 troops and nearly all the elephants. One of the most difficult stages of the trip was to the Pass of Moncenisio, at 6,000 feet. Many of the elephants perished there under the snow. In fact, archaeologists from several countries have taken advantage of recent melting glaciers in that area to unearth numerous remains of *Proboscidea* who perished due to the harsh conditions of the journey.

Combat

The Carthaginians arrived in Italy with little appetite for war. Hannibal was determined to justify so much suffering. And he did just that! Urged on by its veterans, his army won the first battles, Cannae in 216 B.C. and at Lake Trasimene in 217 B.C., and at Cannae in the following year. This last is still studied in military academies. But the Carthaginian army had been seriously weakened by its Alpine adventure and finally went down to defeat at the Battle of Zama, against an army of legionnaires led by Scipio Africanus. The battle left 5,000 Romans dead, and more than 20,000 Carthaginian corpses. Carthage was forced to surrender under humiliating conditions that included military disarmament and the disbanding of its fleet. The long squabbling came to an end with the Third Punic War (149–146 B.C.). Rome could brook no rival and finished by literally sweeping the valiant Carthaginian civilization off the face of the earth.

A shivering Carthaginian soldier freezes on the back of an elephant. At some point Hannibal's army must have had second thoughts about the wisdom of his plan.

Crossing the Alps

Hannibal's exact route across the Alps is not known. Most theories are based on the texts of Polybius and Livy. But if you are adventurous and want to follow in his footsteps the most likely mountain passes are as follows:

- San Bernardo
- Mont-Cenis
- Montgenèvre
- La Croix

Why choose one over the other? Based on the information provided by ancient accounts, it seems most likely that Hannibal chose Montgenèvre for the following reasons:

1. It was wide enough to accommodate an expedition of this magnitude.

2. The defile was short enough so that the army could debouch on the same day they broke camp.

3. The road to Italy was oriented to the north.

4. The first part of the descent path was narrow and steep.

5. There was a less pronounced decline for about 30 miles since it took Hannibal three days to get to the plain.

6. Italy is visible from the top (per Polybius) or from somewhere in the beginning of the descent (according to Livy).

So cheer up, now you just need to find a few elephants. . . and hope that the weather doesn't turn against you.

Love Can Be Deadly

ERROR: Mixing Romance and Politics.

When?
48–30 B.C.
in Ptolemaic
Egypt

Who?
Cleopatra,
Julius Caesar and
Mark Anthony.

Consequences
The violent deaths of
three people, convulsions
in the Roman state, and
the disappearance of the
Ptolemaic dynasty.

Age cannot wither her, nor custom stale
Her infinite variety: other women cloy
The appetites they feed: but she makes
*   hungry*
Where most she satisfies; for vilest things
come themselves in her: that the holy priests
Bless her when she is riggish.

Antony and Cleopatra,
William Shakespeare

The history of ancient Rome contributes to many soap operas, but the affairs of the Egyptian queen Cleopatra VII (69–30 b.c.), first with Julius Caesar (100–44 b.c.) and later with Mark Antony (83–30 b.c.), are much more delicious and intriguing. Nea Cleopatra Thea Philopator (something like "the goddess who loves her father") comes down in history as being the last reigning monarch of Egypt, although her son Caesarion was the nominal Pharaoh until the country's annexation by Augustus.

But let us go back a bit. When the father of Cleopatra (Ptolemy XII Auletes) died, the throne was left to his two children: Cleopatra was eighteen years old at the time, her brother Ptolemy XIII only twelve. In order to preserve harmony within the kingdom, the young siblings married each other (this was probably their father's intention). Cleopatra was please to share wealth and power with her brat of a younger brother, and for the first year their reign was fairly peaceful. But things started to get ugly in Egypt. Drought, poor harvests and famine ravaged the country. Cleopatra was accused of displaying an overly conciliatory attitude to the dreaded Rome. Her

Cleopatra, a Hollywood extravaganza, starred Elizabeth Taylor, Richard Burton, and Rex Harrison as Caesar.

Cleopatra, queen of kings and the daughter of kings, from a coin from 32 b.c.

brother Ptolemy took advantage of popular discontent and drove his sister from the throne. But Cleopatra was not one to waste time; exiled in Syria, she gathered an army to regain power.

Caesar meets Cleopatra

Meanwhile, the Roman Republic was engaged in one of its periodic civil wars. Julius Caesar and Pompey fought for power until the legions of the latter fell in the Battle of Pharsalus (Greece). Pompey fled to Egypt, but there ended up literally losing his head. Ptolemy XIII had ordered him to be beheaded to gain favor with Caesar and his help in defeating his ambitious sister Cleopatra. Bad decision, because Caesar was enraged upon hearing of Pompey's death. Despite their rivalry, they had been longtime friends and, in fact, Nonetheless, Caesar agreed to act as arbiter in the Ptolemy family conflict. Cleopatra, however, used her considerable powers of seduction to "persuade" Caesar and obtain his support. It is said that she was conveyed into Caesar's rooms rolled up naked in a luxurious carpet laid at his feet by the Sicilian Apollodorus. The truth is that they spent a few nights together and Cleopatra became pregnant with Caesarion, son of Julius Caesar (though unrecognized by him).

These affairs only served to increase the en-

Statue of Julius Caesar.
Cleopatra seduced him. He brought her to Rome but did not divorce his wife.

mity of Cleopatra's now cuck-olded husband-brother. He went to war to turn the people against their queen. The tensions mounted until 20,000 soldiers besieged the royal palace where Caesar and Cleopatra were staying. The war lasted several months and ended when Rome crushed the insurgency; the young Ptolemy drowned in the mud of the Nile.

The way was now clear for Cleopatra to regain the throne. Although she finally had to marry another brother (Ptolemy XIV), he was nothing more than her puppet. She continued her relationship with Julius Caesar and even traveled a few times with her son Caesarion to Rome, where she lived as a concubine (given that Caesar was already married to the Roman, Calpurnia). Their relationship raised many eyebrows, and rumors began to spread that Caesar and Cleopatra wanted to reign jointly in Rome and Egypt and thus control the whole Mediterranean. During Cleopatra's second visit to Rome on March 15, 44 B.C., Julius Caesar was assassinated by a group of senators wary of such absolutist intentions. The plot thickened, however, with the entrance of a new lover for Cleopatra: Mark Antony.

The first movie version of Cleopatra dates from 1917. It starred Theda Bara as the royal temptress. It was destroyed for its salacious content. Only a few frames remain in the archives of the Museum of Modern Art.

Cleopatra meets Mark Antony
With the death of Julius Caesar, Cleopa-

Giovanni Batista Tiepolo painted Anthony and Cleopatra in the costumes of his own time.

tra returned to Egypt and without further ado poisoned her husband Ptolemy XIV and put her four-year-old son Caesarion on the throne, with her assuming the role of regent. Meanwhile, in Rome things were happening quickly. With Caesar dead, two opposing camps were formed. On one side were Caesar's assassins, who saw themselves as "liberators." They were led by Brutus and Gaius Cassius. On the other stood the triumvirate of Octavian (political heir appointed by Julius Caesar in his will), Lepidus (former general of Caesar's cavalry) and Mark Antony (commander of his army). The triumvirate defeated Brutus's army at the Battle of Philippi.

Antony turned his attention eastward. War, however, is expensive, and Antony went to Egypt to request economic aid from Cleopatra. There, just as his mentor Julius Caesar, Antony fell subject to the charms of the Egyptian queen, with whom he enjoyed a torrid winter. From that meeting, Cleopatra became pregnant with twins (Cleopatra Selene II and Alexander Helios). However, Antony returned to Rome and ended up marrying his fiancée Octavia. Still, he did not forget his Egyptian queen, whom he married four years later in Egypt (without divorcing his first wife). Together they had another son (Ptolemy Philadelphus) and began a life of luxury.

A tragic end

Such indulgence on the part of a Roman at the hands of a capricious foreign queen was the perfect excuse for the ambitious Octavian to set the people of Rome against his rival. Serious charges were hurled back and forth, until finally the Roman Senate declared war on Egypt in 32 B.C. In less than a year, Mark Antony's troops were defeated at the naval Battle of Actium, and Cleopatra took to her heels. What followed is worthy of a Shakespearean drama: Antony was falsely informed of the death of Cleopatra and plunged a sword into his belly. Octavian captured Cleopatra and planned to display her in his triumphal procession. He ordered a watch set to prevent her suicide. But the queen refused to die as a slave. She managed to smuggle an asp into her chambers and died from its bite. Her dramatic (and romantic) death signaled the end of the Ptolemaic Dynasty. Egypt would become a province under the control of Roman Empire until its dissolution, and Cleopatra would go down in history as an ambitious, alluring and independent woman who was able to keep at bay one of the most powerful civilizations in history. She did, however, pay a high price: the destruction of her country. History and legend concur that she was an unparalleled beauty and unequalled in the mastery of the arts of love.

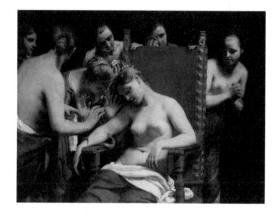

Above Bas-relief showing the suicide of Mark Antony after the Battle of Actium. The best-known account is somewhat romantic, blaming his suicide on his love for Cleopatra. In actuality, he fled and killed himself later on. **Below:** Cleopatra in a seventeenth-century painting by Guido Cagnacci.

Don't Go into the Office Today, Dear.

ERROR: Going into the senate unprotected despite numerous warnings and predictions of his death.

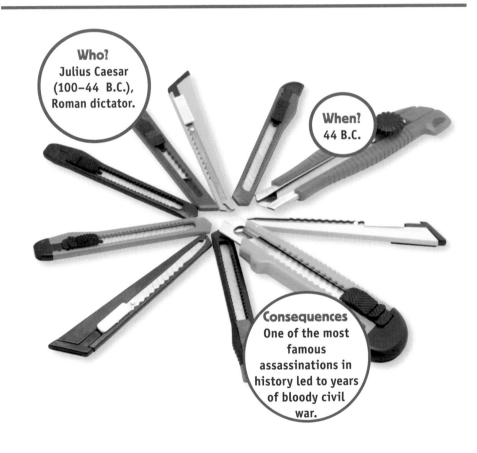

Who?
Julius Caesar (100–44 B.C.), Roman dictator.

When?
44 B.C.

Consequences
One of the most famous assassinations in history led to years of bloody civil war.

One finds it also related by many, that a soothsayer bade him prepare for some great danger on the Ides of March. When the day was come, Caesar, as he went to the senate, met this soothsayer, and said to him by way of raillery, "The Ides of March are come;" who answered him calmly, "Yes, they are come, but they are not past."

Parallel Lives,
Plutarch

No doubt Julius Caesar was a brave fellow, but he ended up going too far. Convinced that the goddess Fortuna would never leave him, he went through life with supreme self-confidence until a few senators killed him.

Gaius Julius Caesar was born on July 13, 100 B.C. into a somewhat impoverished patrician family. Family connections propelled him through the *cursus honorum*, the sequence of governmental positions which those headed for high office were bound to follow. Caesar held the positions of quaestor, magistrate, pontifex maximus, praetor and finally, consul. As consul Caesar was granted control of several provinces. During this

Film poster from Joseph Mankiewicz's production of Shakespeare's *Julius Caesar*.

time, he engineered the conquest of Gaul, Britain and Germany. For eight long years, his troops fought continuously against a total of three million Helvetiis, Gauls, Germans and Britons. Alexander the Great left his mark on history because of the enormous territory he conquered. Caesar's campaigns, however, had an even greater influence on Western culture. His conquests led to the Romanization of almost all what we think of today as Western Europe. Never had one man had managed victories of such magnitude.

Born to win

Caesar's prestige and military power created troubles in Rome. There was considerable civil unrest and his political enemies could not come up with a plan to force Caesar to disband his army. They finally accused him of treason and publicly called for his exile. The general was particularly incensed that the opposition movement was led by Pompey, his former friend and political ally. On January 13, 49 B.C. he crossed the Rubicon, uttering the famous phrase, "the die is cast." His troops followed shouting: "Caesar or nothing!"

This act launched a civil war that lasted for three years (49–46 b.c.). Caesar emerged as victor once more. He first captured Rome and subdued Italy; then he took Spain, and finally, he went in pursuit of Pompey, who had sought refuge in the East. He was saved the work of bringing his enemy to bay by the Egyptian pharaoh, who had Pompey beheaded. His next move was to invade Pontus. His swift victory over King Pharnaces is commemorated in his famous phrase "Veni, vidi, vici" ("I came, I saw, I conquered"). Before returning to Rome, he had time to defeat the last of Pompey's supporters resisting in Africa (Battle of Thapsus 46 B.C.) and Pompey's children in Hispania (Battle of

Munda, 45 B.C.). After all this work, one would think he would be ready to retire. Not at all. Once back in Rome, Caesar started to reorganize its institutions, improve provincial government and offer Roman citizenship to all its inhabitants. He distributed lands among his troops, as Suetonius tells us in *The Twelve Caesars*:

> *To every foot soldier in his veteran legions besides the 2,000 sesterces paid him in the beginning of the Civil War he gave 20,000 more in the shape of prize money. He likewise allotted them lands, but not in contiguity, that the former owners might not be entirely dispossessed. To the people of Rome, he gave 300 sesterces a man which he had formerly promised them, and 100 more to each for the delay in fulfilling his engagement. He likewise remitted a year's rent due to the treasury for such houses in Rome as did not pay above 2,000 sesterces a year, and through the rest of Italy for all such as did not exceed in yearly rent 500 sesterces. To all this he added a public entertainment and a distribution of meat, and after his Spanish victory two public dinners. For considering the first he had given as too sparing and unsuited to this profuse liberality he five days afterwards added another which was most plentiful.*

Julius Caesar was a military genius. His *Commentaries on the Gallic Wars* are an enduring record of his mastery of tactics and strategy.

At the time of his death, Caesar had become a kind of demigod, assuming titles such as Perpetual Dictator, Censor, Father of the Nation and Pontiff Maximus. No

How could such a brilliant strategist have fallen into such a simple trap?

mean accomplishment. The only thing lacking was the title of king, but this was already too much for a number republican senators, who began to forge a plot against his life.

Beware the Ides of March

Julius Caesar occupies a prominent place in this book on historical blunders because of his decision to attend the Senate the day of his death. He had abundant reasons not to go to work that day. Authors such as Suetonius and Plutarch record numerous warnings that Caesar received about the plot to murder him. There were also signs and omens. It was as if he overlooked a neon sign at the entrance to the forum. The night before, his wife Calpurnia dreamed of his death; a soothsayer warned him of the many inauspicious omens with the famous remark: "Beware the Ides of March!" His friends begged him not to attend the Senate that day. He was beginning to have second thoughts, but his friend Brutus persuaded him to proceed. Caesar seemed emboldened, not chastened. It was on his way to the senate that he met the soothsayer who delivered his prescient warning. Caesar mocked him, observing that the Ides had come and he was no worse for it. To which the seer replied: "They have come, but they are not past." Despite the repeated admonitions, he took no precautions, not even accepting protection.

The day of the assassination

Once inside the Senate everything happened very fast. The first one to approach him was Tullius Cimber (governor of Bithynia and Pontus). He ripped Caesar's toga, pleading with him to annul his brother's exile. This was the signal for a somewhat clumsy and reckless melee. Several senators attacked Caesar, actually stabbing each other in the process. According to Suetoni-

ous, Servilius Casca inflicted the first of twenty-three wounds, of which only one, the second, was actually mortal. Covered in blood, Gaius Julius Caesar died with dignity. He wrapped his toga around his head and his skirt around his legs that he might not expose himself when he fell. Some authors relate that his last words were "Et tu Brute?"

The senate rejoicing at the death of Caesar. But his death did not free Rome from tyranny; it was governed by emperors for the rest of its history. Julius Caesar's death signaled the definitive end of the Roman republic.

Greenland? Not Very Green

ERROR: To journey with a few hundred people to a wholly inhospitable land.

When?
985 A.D.

Who?
Erik the Red
(950–1003).

Consequences
The death of more than half of them before they reached their destination.

Viking ships were called dragons. These mythical creatures served as figureheads, symbolizing power and courage.

He sailed back to Iceland the following summer and arrived at the port of Breidafjord. And he gave the country he discovered the name Greenland, because he said that people would be more tempted to go there if the place had an attractive name.

Anonymous,
The Saga of Erik the Red, (XIII century)

Either the Vikings were colorblind or deluded when they claimed to have found a green paradise in the arid lands of Greenland. In any event, they christened the largest island in the world as Gronland ("Greenland"). This autonomous territory now belongs to the kingdom of Denmark. And 80 percent of its land is completely covered with a thick layer of ice (though that may change with global warming).

The first Norse settler of Greenland, Erik Thorvaldsson, was born in Rogaland (Norway) around the year 950. He was

The normal Viking helmet was made of leather. Helmets with horns were rare, reserved for the nobility.

The North Pole as seen in the seventeenth century. This is the earliest known map of the Arctic. Four rivers divide the snowcap, and Greenland appears as much smaller than it really is.

called Erik the Red, probably because of the color of his hair, and had a reputation as a hard man, even among the Vikings. This reputation ran in the family. His father (Thorvald) was charged with murder, and his whole family had to make a sudden departure from Norway, moving to Iceland. They tried to settle down there, but their neighbors were not pleased with the idea. After several skirmishes, Erik followed the family tradition and had to make a quick getaway. He was banished for three years, becoming an exile with nowhere to go.

A good marketing campaign

At that time, Erik had already heard talk of the sighting of new land west of Iceland. Having nothing to lose, he prepared a boat and sailed from Snaefellsnes. Three weeks later he came to the vast expanse of Greenland. He remained there three years and then returned to Iceland with the intention of preparing to go back and establish a permanent settlement there. It was not easy, however, to persuade his countrymen to take their cattle and gather sufficient materials for the new colony. In speaking to prospective settlers he always referred to the land's "Green Earth" in order to further entice them. Even though the climate of the Middle Ages was warmer than the current temperature in these latitudes, Erik thought it would improve his chances to come up with a more attractive name than Iceland. In addition, Iceland was becoming a bit cramped. The lack of land encouraged a total of 700 brave pioneers. In the spring of 985, they departed aboard 25 ships, but the harsh conditions of the voyage was more than many of them had bargained for. Finally, some 300 settlers reached Greenland on board the few ships that had not sunk in the North Atlantic. Once there, they saw the promised land was not as promised, but since there was no room for them in Iceland (even if they had had the strength to return), they established two colonies: Vestribyggd (the Western Settlement, near present-day Godthab), and Eystribyggd (the Eastern Settlement). In the latter, Erik founded the town of Brattahlid. From there he ruled his colonies as Paramount Chieftain, a respectable title that represented the colony's independence from Iceland. Among the settlers was Erik's son Leif Ericsson, who gradually assumed command of a disaffected people who felt cheated by their leader. At its peak, the population reached 5,000. During summers, armies of men were sent north of the Arctic Circle to hunt for food that included seals, walruses and whales. Erik the Red died in 1003, victim of an epidemic that ravaged the colony. And the final decline came with another disease: the Black Death (1348) which, together with attacks from the Inuits and general starvation put a definitive end to the colony. It is also believed that in the Little Ice Age of the fourteenth century the settlers, unlike the Inuits, were unable to adapt to the falling temperature. In our time several excavations in Brattahlid (currently located in the town of Qassiarsuk) have found some traces of the Viking settlement, including a Christian church and 150 skeletons corresponding to a strong and tall people, like Scandinavians today.

Statue of Erik the Red shows him scanning the horizon and looking into the future.

The End Is Near (Again)

ERROR: Interpreting social, economic or natural phenomena as signs of the end of the world.

Who? Christian believers in Europe.

When? December 31, 999.

Consequences Widespread panic.

And I saw an angel coming down out of heaven, having the key to the Abyss and holding in his hand a great chain. He seized the dragon, that ancient serpent, who is the devil, or Satan, and bound him for a thousand years. He threw him into the Abyss, and locked and sealed it over him, to keep him from deceiving the nations anymore until the thousand years were ended. After that, he must be set free for a short time.

Revelation 20:1–3

"Danse Macabre" in the year 1000, a convenient date for the end of the world.

In times of great confusion there arise prophets that declare all is lost, the end is near. They point to devastat-

Greeting the year 1000. If heavenly trumpets sounded, they did not presage anything here on earth.

The Four Horsemen of the Apocalypse: **Conquest, War, Starvation and Death in a painting by Viktor Vasnetsov.**

ing plagues, rains of fire, Antichrists, solar eclipses or the appearance of comets. It is important at such times to select a date in the calendar — that seems to add credibility — proclaim the news and send the world a message of hope for the end of days.

To be living as the year 1000 was just about to dawn was not easy; in fact, it was much easier to die: epidemics, wars and famine decimated a fearful population that looked upon all these as omens of the dark designs of fate. This was a time when the great bulk of mankind was illiterate. Their only sources of information were from Sunday Mass, the edicts of their rulers and rumors going round the town square. At the start of the new millennium, the power in Europe was in the hands of the Holy Roman Emperor (Otto III) and the Holy See

(led by Pope Sylvester II). There is considerable documentation pertaining to both the religious and temporal powers, and it doesn't seem that they were particularly preoccupied with fears about the end of the world. But believers saw things differently. They were terrified of Judgment Day and the tribulations that were to precede it. Visionaries arose tossing off prophecies left and right describing visions that only they were able to see. As the chronicler Raoul Glaber reported in the middle of the eleventh century (1048):

> *After the many miraculous signs that preceded the end of the first millennium, there was no lack of ingenious and sharp-witted men who attested to phenomena of great significance in relation to the proximity of the millennium. . . The world, as a punishment for the sins of men, was prey to disastrous scourges. It was believed that the order of the seasons and the elements, reigning from the beginning of time, had become forever relegated to chaos and that this was the end of mankind.*

A pact with the devil could bring youth and power but at the cost of one's soul. Pope Sylvester II was accused of selling the souls of his flock and hastening the end of the world.

Pope Sylvester II became a target of accusations and suspicion. The first French pope in history (Auvergne, 945–Rome, 1003) was a real scholar: an outstanding theologian, philosopher, mathematician and inventor. He has gone down in history as an early proponent of the Indo-Arabic decimal system in Europe, inventor of abacuses, astrolabes, water clocks, strange cryptograms and other original contributions. He studied Arabic treatises on mathematics and translations of Aristotle during an extended stay in Spain.

As his papacy coincided with the change of millennium, he came to be linked with the widespread superstitious fears haunting Europe towards the end of the last decade of the tenth century. Victor Hugo in his *La Legende des siècles* (1859) paints a fine picture of this period. Other more credulous writers like the chronicler William of Malmesbury asserted that Sylvester II had reached the throne of Saint Peter thanks to a pact with the devil! However, William reported that, at the time of his death, the pope felt remorse and ordered that his body be cut into pieces and not be buried in consecrated ground. This fabricated story was held to be true for almost seven centuries until his tomb was finally opened in 1648. They found Sylvester II with the miter on his head and hands crossed on a body almost wholly intact.

Happy New Year

Michael Pacher, *Church Fathers Altarpiece* (detail). This painting shows either St. Wolfgang or St. Augustine with the devil.

Faced with contemporary reports of utter disaster, it is not surprising that the public became anxious. The apostle John's Book of Revelation was scrutinized for signs of the times, and prophetic visions multiplied. In the late tenth century, unusual facts were interpreted as an ominous signs, such as: an epidemic that took place in northern Italy in 997 and caused intense skin irritations; a great famine due to a consecutive series of poor harvests; feudal wars between France and Italy; the Norman invasions; and other natural phenomenon, like the comet in 1000 that remained visible in the sky over Europe for three months. All these events tended to assume an exaggerated importance in religious ceremonies (such as liturgies, sermons and preaching). Slowly, the belief spread that all this

was happening because of humanity's sins.

By the end of the year 999 every household was seized with dreadful expectation. Many people sought refuge in churches, where they awaited the appearance of the Antichrist. Apparently he was busy with other matters, because that night ended, and the world awoke just as good (or bad) as it had always been on January 1, 1000. Of course, it took a while to forget the millennial fears. And then we all began worrying about the next millennium. . . in which everyone would be prepared, as discussed later in this book, for the computer to end civilization as we know it.

Hans Memling, *The Last Judgment*, c. 1470. Triptych, central panel. When the clock struck midnight they could have uncorked the champagne, except that Dom Perignon would not be born for a few centuries.

Leaning Tower of Pisa

ERROR: To build a tower on shaky ground with insufficient reinforcement.

Who?
Bonanno Pisano, sculptor and architect.

When?
1173–1999 in Pisa.

Consequences
The Tower has progressively tilted almost fifteen feet off of vertical. On the other hand, it has certainly attracted tourism, netting the city millions of dollars each year.

Founded by the Greeks in the fifth century B.C., the strategic commercial port of Pisa prospered. Residents and merchants lived high on the hog taking advantage of trade with Tuscany, Sardinia, Corsica and the French and Spanish coasts. Money and power have always gone hand in hand, and the maritime republic of Pisa began to grow in power. By the Middle Ages it had conquered territory and started colonies in Antioch, Tripoli, Constantinople, Alexandria and Cairo. Its crowning achievement was to wrest Palermo from the Saracens. This resulted in a stunning influx of wealth. The Pisan authorities decided to build a cathedral worthy of so powerful a city. They disdained half-measures and planned an ambitious building program of four structures: the Duomo Cathedral, the Baptistery, the Tower and the Camposanto. At this point things began to get more complicated.

The footsteps of visitors have scooped out the tower's stairs over the course of the centuries.

Work begins

In 1063, the architect Buscheto started construction on the Cathedral of Santa Maria Assunta, in the center of the Piazza dei Miracoli (declared a World Heritage Site in 1987). The Pisans were constantly competing with Venice, another powerful Italian city-state. The idea was to surpass the Basilica of San Marco in beauty and magnificence. They acquired expensive marbles, stunning granite columns (appropriated from the mosque at Palermo), elaborate frescos and lots of bronze inlays. The result was one of the finest works of Romanesque architecture.

A century later work began on the baptistery. Under the supervision of architect Diotisalvi, Pisa could soon boast of a building 100 feet in diameter, all covered with marble, the largest ever built in Italy. So far so good. Pisans were filled with civic pride at this magnificent achievement. And then they began on the Duomo's bell tower.

Something is not right

Although some have suggested that the inclination of the Tower was actually premeditated, it seems clear that it was intended to climb straight up into the sky. Given the immense cost of the project, there was no room for architectural jokes or postmodern experiments. The credit for the construction has gone to the Italian Bonanno Pisano, who, if he wasn't already dead, would die of shame (or laughter) if by lifting his head (he was buried at the base of the tower) he could see such structural disaster. The first three levels of the Tower of Pisa (out of a total of eight) were completed between 1173 and 1178. The foundation was very weak (only ten feet deep) and the subsoil, made of fine sand and clay, extremely unstable. Things began to go south. Work was halted for a hundred years!

Meanwhile, to avoid boredom, the Pisans devoted themselves to war with neighboring states. For once, war produced something good: the long interruption allowed the soil to settle and kept the tower from collapsing.

But after a century they hit upon what they thought would be a solution: what if we build the upper floors with one side taller than the other and so straighten the tower? No sooner said than done. Between 1272 and 1278 they returned to work and a century later completed the bell tower. They had rectified one problem by curving the tower to its current inclination. What a mess! It looked like a 15,000-ton pendulum rather than a monument to the glory of a powerful city. The more effort put in to straightening it, the more twisted it became. To make matters worse, in 1838, the architect Alessandro Della Gherardesca excavated a path around its base to improve its appearance. The vents caused flooding which in turn increased the tower's inclination. It then had to suffer from the technical expertise of Benito Mussolini's engineers. They attempted to strengthen the walls inside the tower. . . and the concrete edifice tilted an additional foot! The inclination was critical, but far from condemning the whole enterprise, the Tower began to attract thousands of tourists from around the world. Of course, it had to be seen to be believed. Every day hundreds of people climbed up and down its 294 steps until January 7, 1990 when the decision was reached to close the tower to the public for fear of a possible collapse. An international group of specialists, engineers and mathematicians was convened to see if the tower could be stabilized without losing its characteristic tilt. No easy task, since at that time the tower was leaning 14.66 feet with respect to the base.

800 years later...

A curse hung over Pisa. In 1993 the city agreed to add 630 tons of lead to the north side, to counteract its southward tilt. It seemed to work, but the aesthetic effect was appalling. It endured a couple of years in this fashion and in 1995 the engineers tried to stabilize the subsoil of the sunken side (south) using liquid nitrogen to replace the soft ground by something harder. This only made matters worse. The solution? Put 250 tons of lead on the other side.

Finally, in 1999 (over 800 years after work had begun), the tower was stabilized by removing 125 feet of sandy soil under the bell tower on the opposite side, thus allowing the Tower to settle on that side. Eleven years and 27 million dollars later, the edifice was reopened to the public. Currently, the Tower is being carefully monitored. They say that it will remain stable for the next 300 years. Only time will tell.

Of course, with this solution, the Tower of Pisa has lost its pride of place as the most steeply inclined historic building. The honor now goes to a simple bell tower built in 1450 in the small town of Suurhusen (Germany). I do not know what the builders were thinking, but its structure inclines to 0.5 degrees more than the famous Italian tower. Anyone want to volunteer to straighten it?

Welcome to Japan

ERROR: Columbus disembarks in the West Indies convinced that he had reached Japan.

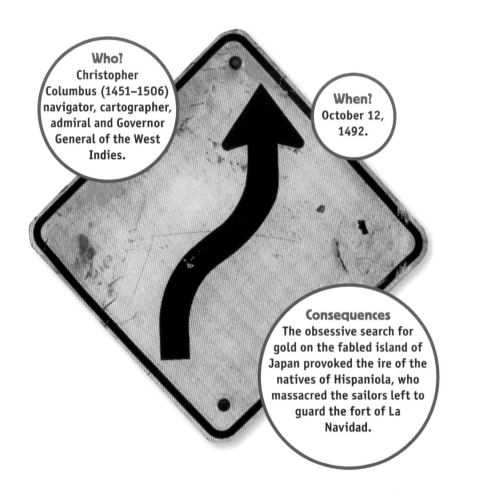

Who?
Christopher Columbus (1451–1506) navigator, cartographer, admiral and Governor General of the West Indies.

When?
October 12, 1492.

Consequences
The obsessive search for gold on the fabled island of Japan provoked the ire of the natives of Hispaniola, who massacred the sailors left to guard the fort of La Navidad.

Genoese, Portuguese, Catalan, Galician, Andalusian. . . many have claimed the honor of being the birthplace of the famous explorer. He has gone down in history as the discoverer of the New World, even though it was in error. What was America doing there? Columbus wanted to catch sight of Cipango (present-day Japan) and the lands of the Great Khan. But he was a little disoriented and thought he could get there from the opposite direction, that is, by traveling west. Apparently his obsession began around 1480, while reading the work of the Florentine mathematician and physician Paolo dal Pozzo Toscanelli. Toscanelli maintained that one could reach the Indies by heading west from Europe. He had even drawn a map marking the route, based on the travels of Marco Polo. Notwithstanding the famous Venetian traveler, Toscanelli seriously miscalculated the diameter of the earth, claiming that the distance from the western tip of Europe (Lisbon) to Asia (Quinsay or current day Hangzhou, China) was much less than it actually is.

Christopher Columbus before Queen Isabella. Historians think, but are not sure, that Columbus was Italian by birth. In soliciting support for his voyage, he first approached the Portuguese crown. When he was rebuffed, he sought out the queen of Spain. She gave him three ships and a share of the profits from the trip.

Good business

Let's face it. Medieval Europeans looked to the East with a certain amount of greed. Everywhere, they saw gold, precious stones, and luxurious fabrics. Its overflowing abundance would confer enormous benefits on everyone. The stories of the adventurer Marco

Gold in exchange for disease

The Spanish conquest of the Americas vastly increased European wealth and knowledge of the world's geography. It was not, however, very beneficial to the indigenous peoples of the Western Hemisphere. Countless numbers fell prey to new diseases against which they had no immunity, or they were enslaved by the conquerors.

Polo further confirmed these suppositions. According to Washington Irving's account of Columbus' voyages, the explorer saw the island of Cipango (that is, Japan) as

Abounding in gold, which, however, the king seldom permits to be transported out of the island. The king has a magnificent palace covered with plates of gold, as in other countries the palaces are covered with sheets of lead or copper. The halls and chambers are likewise covered with gold, the windows adorned with it, sometimes in plates of thickness of two fingers. The island also produces vast quantities of the largest and finest pearls, together with a variety of precious stones; The Great Khan made several attempts to conquer this island, but in vain. This island was an object of diligent search to Columbus.

Columbus and others were drawn powerfully to this enchanted island. But how to get there? Medieval Christian Europe had not progressed scientifically very far beyond walking. . . The Arab and Jews were much more advanced. The Islamic world had lived through its golden age in the seventh and eighth centuries. Its scientists were devoted to the study

Columbus shows a group of Spanish nobles how to stand an egg on one end to demonstrate that once you know how to do something, it becomes easy.

of astronomy, expert in the construction and use of astrolabes. Muslim sages concluded that the earth was spherical, although some still maintained that the sun and universe revolved around it. For their part, the Jews also studied the stars, but their primary interest was in cartography. Europe came to serve as the intersection of the three communities (Christians, Arabs and Jews) taking the very best from each. The Spanish were experts at that. During the thirteenth and fourteenth centuries, monarchs such as James I, Peter III, James II and Pedro IV of Aragon, supported mainly Jewish scholars in their endeavors in mapping and navigation. There was fierce competition: Venetians, Florentines, Genoese, Pisans, Catalans; everyone wanted a piece of the pie. The first attempts to reach the Indies across the uncharted ocean were complete failures. The Genoese tried unsuccessfully at the end of thirteenth century. The brothers Ugolino and Vadino Vivaldi set off from the Strait of Gibraltar in two galleons. They were never heard from again. In the end it was Spain that had the first great success.

Pursuing his dream

After numerous failures, Europe was beginning to run out of resources. With the capture of Constantinople by the Turks in 1453 and their subsequent domination of Egypt, things became even more difficult. Christian trade routes were blocked, and European merchants had to find new ways to reach the coveted East Indies. The *Mare Tenebrosum* (Atlantic) seemed fearsome, but still the attempt had to be made. The known world ended in the Finisterre and then nothing but darkness. Castille and Portugal emerged as the dominant powers. Under the lead of Henry the Navigator, Portugal began to explore the Atlantic coast of Africa looking for a way to skirt the southern tip and head for India. These efforts encouraged the young Christopher Columbus, who was presented at the court of King John II, in an ambitious project: to put together three ships with provisions and goods to trade in the East Indies. He asked to be appointed Admiral and Governor of the discovered territories and awarded ten percent of the profits. The Portuguese king was less than wholehearted

Columbus claims possession of the New World upon making land. The priests immediately set out to convert the inhabitants. As to his discoveries, it's clear that he did not have the slightest idea of where he was.

in his support, and the expedition never got off the ground.

To make matters worse, Columbus' wife died. In 1485, he left Portugal. But he could not ignore the lure of the riches of the East. On January 20, 1486, Columbus offered his services to the Catholic Monarchs of Spain. They agreed that they would think about it, and this they did for the next six years. Finally, in April 1492, thanks to Isabella, who was much more enterprising than her husband, Ferdinand, the famous Capitulations of Santa Fe were formalized. Christopher Columbus was named Admiral, Viceroy and Governor General of all the territories discovered. And yes, he was awarded ten percent of the profits.

On to Japan

All the preparations completed, Columbus and 87 men boarded their three ships and left the port of Palos de la Frontera (Huelva) the morning of August 3, 1492, searching for a new route to the Indies. They set sail to the Canaries and once there traveled westward, convinced they were headed to Cipango (Japan) and Cathay (China). Three months later, at dawn on October 12, 1492 the lead ship

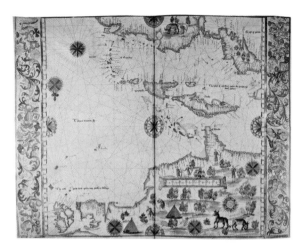

sighted the coast of San Salvador (Guanahani, Bahamas). Columbus landed and took possession of the island for Spain, certain he had set foot on the first island of the Indies of Asia. Subsequently, the ships visited Santa Maria de la Concepción (Rum Cay, Bahamas), Fernandina (Long Island), Isabela (Crooked Island) and finally Cuba, which he named Juana Island. But where was Japan? And the lavish residence of the Great Khan? According to his estimates Japan was about 2,750 miles west of the Canary Islands. He traveled through many islands in the Caribbean until he arrived at a large island that he named Hispaniola (present day Haiti and Dominican Republic), which would become Spain's first colony in the New World. Columbus died after several more trips without ever realizing his mistake. It was not until years later that the Italian navigator Amerigo Vespucci realized that a new and unknown continent existed. One had to cross another ocean to get to Japan.

A medieval map of the Americas and the West Indies offers a curious view of the territory. It serves to emphasize the navigational difficulties in an age before there was a way to measure longitude.

The Gods Have Landed

ERROR: To think that Hernán Cortés was the god Quetzalcoatl and hand over one's entire empire to him in a fit of superstitious panic.

When?
November 9, 1519.

Who?
Moctezuma Xocoyotzin (1466–1520, known as Montezuma), Aztec Emperor.

Consequences
The destruction of the Aztec Empire and the conquest of Mexico by the Spanish.

Motecusuma continued as follows: "I am perfectly well aware, Malinche, [Cortés] what the people of Tlascalla, with whom you are so closely allied, have been telling you respecting myself. They have made you believe that I am a species of god, and that my palaces are filled with gold, silver, and jewels. I do not think, for an instant, that reasonable men as you are can put any faith in all their talk, besides which, you can now convince yourself that I am made of flesh and bone as you are, and that my palaces are built of stone, lime, and wood. I am, to be sure, a powerful monarch; it is likewise true that I have inherited vast treasures from my ancestors; but with regard to anything else they may have told you respecting me, it is all nonsense.

From an eyewitness account

By the fifteenth century, the Mexica (or Aztecs as they are better known) were a powerful people. Their state, Mexico-Tenochtitlan, extended through the area that is now Mexico City. Its dependencies included other towns in the region, such as Tlacopan and Texcoco. It could boast of a solid political, social, economic and religious structure. The reach of its empire extended through much of central and southern Mexico. The population of the city of Tenochtitlan is estimated to have been about 230,000, which made it larger than most European cities of its time. Constantinople had about 200,000 residents, Paris and Venice 185,000 and 130,000 respectively.

The ruler of such splendor was the Emperor Montezuma II. The chronicler Bernal Díaz del Castillo who was present during the first meeting of the emperor with Europeans described the event as follows:

Montezuma was a great king and a great man but very superstitious. All of the omens turned against him with the arrival of the Spaniards.

Motecusuma himself, according to his custom, was sumptuously attired, had on a species of half boot, richly set with jewels, and whose soles were made of solid gold. The four grandees who supported him were also richly attired. Besides these distinguished caziques, there were many other grandees around the monarch, some of whom held the canopy over his head, while others again occupied the road before him, and spread cotton cloths on the ground that his feet might not touch the bare earth. No one of his suite ever looked at him full in the face; every one in his presence stood with eyes downcast.

Everything was fine until April 1, 1519, when some of

Omens and signs

Montezuma was extremely superstitious, and his fears were fanned by numerous evil omens. According to the Codex Florentino, written by Fray Bernardino de Sahagún in the sixteenth century, eight signs announced the end of the Aztec empire:

1. A column of fire (probably a comet) appeared in the night sky.
2. The temple of Huitzilopochtli was destroyed by fire.
3. Lightning struck the temple of Xiuhtecuhtli, but no thunder was heard.
4. Fire fell from heaven in broad daylight. Divided into three parts, going from west to east in a long line, loud noises like bells rang throughout the city.
5. The lake's water seemed to boil, as the wind blew and flooded part of Tenochtitlan.
6. Funereal dirges were heard by the people.
7. A strange crane-like bird was caught in a hunt. When Montezuma looked into its eyes, he saw foreign warriors mounted on a kind of deer.
8. Montezuma was visited in his chambers by various apparitions.

the emperor's subjects arrived at court with an alarming rumor. On the Gulf Coast, in the direction of Vera Cruz, strange men had appeared. They had white skin, were blond, bearded and traveled in canoes as large as houses. This was the Spanish expedition led by Hernán Cortés. A total of 400 men landed in what is now known as Puerto de Veracruz (San Juan de Ullua). That day was the beginning of the end of the Aztec empire. And what was even worse, it was written in the stars.

A god appears on Earth

Following the arrival of the Europeans, the Emperor sent emissaries to consult with the three major Aztec gods: Tezcatlipoca, Tlaloc and Quetzalcoatl. The king was convinced that Hernán Cortés was a kind of divine representative on Earth. He thought that if the Spanish allowed him to adorn them with some of the gods' attributes it would strengthen his power since no one would dare adorn a god without having divine authorization to do so. With every sign of cordiality Cortés accepted the ornaments of the god Quetzalcoatl. But Montezuma, realizing the implications of the exchange, began to feel afraid.

Human sacrifice was an integral part of pre-Columbian Mexican culture.

To pay homage to these foreign gods, the Emperor sent them valuable gifts in hopes that these would see the newcomers on their way. But that simply aroused the Spaniards' greed. They were amazed by Aztec wealth. Other exchanges further fueled the Aztec's fear. At one point Cortés sent Montezuma a rusty helmet with instructions that it should be filled with gold. A request that seemed to recall demands made by Huitzilopochtli, chief god of the Aztecs.

Easy pickings

On November 8, 1519, Cortés and Montezuma finally met face to face in Tenochtitlan. The Emperor was more convinced

The Aztecs were very powerful up to the arrival of the Spanish, although their strength was somewhat diminished by local wars.

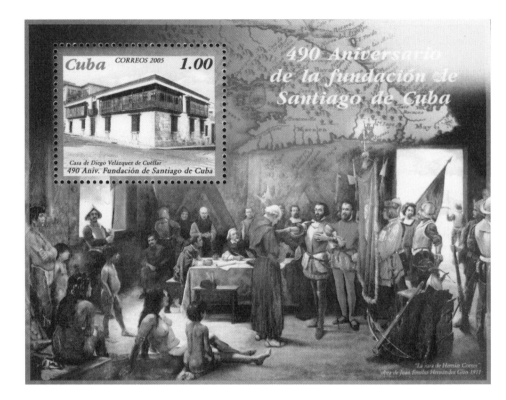

Emilio Hernandez Giro, *The Pledge of Cortés,* 1911.

than ever that the Spaniard was the representative of Quetzalcoatl. Fearful, he yielded to all of his demands. To begin with, he opened his palace to the 400 Spaniards and their horses along with 3,000 of their Indian allies. Once there, the visitors were given rich presents and treated as real divinities.

But soon Cortés grew bored. He decided to do what he knew best: conquer. To the astonishment of the Aztecs, Cortés and his men kidnapped the godlike ruler and held him hostage inside the palace. The same day, Cortés headed for the royal treasury. The emperor himself escorted his captors to the room that held his immense wealth. The foreigners had overthrown the emperor; they were now in total control.

A bridge too far

Meanwhile Cortés had absented himself from the city to repel an attack by Panfilo de Narvaez. Narvaez had been sent by Diego Velazquez, the governor of Cuba, to arrest Cortés. He failed in the attempt, but that's another story. The point is that Cortés had left one Pedro Alvarado in command of Tenochtitlan. It seemed clear to him that the population would remain peaceful as long as they thought Montezuma was in the hands of the gods. But could he be certain that this was the case? The Spaniards were far too weak to resist an angry populace. Alvarado became nervous and decided the best defense is a good offense. During a religious festival in the city, the Spanish set upon the celebrants, killing everyone in sight.

Hernán Cortés wrote several letters to Charles V, King of Spain, requesting support for his efforts to convert the native peoples.

La Noche Triste

The unprovoked attack led by Pedro Alvarado, known as the Massacre of the Templo Mayor, on May 20, 1520, turned the Aztecs against the Spanish invaders once and for all. On his return, Cortés tried to calm down the situation, but his efforts were to no avail. He urged his "puppet" Montezuma to present himself before the people. This further enraged them; they began to throw stones, arrows and everything they had at hand. Montezuma was fatally wounded and died shortly after. Immediately, the Aztecs named Cuitlahuac as their new ruler, and he did not waste any time. He enlisted troops and sought alliances with other peoples to destroy the Spanish invaders. The Spanish troops were besieged in the palace of Axayácatl. So on the night of June 30, 1520 they decided to attempt an escape. Despite their efforts at concealment, their plan was discovered, and the Aztecs were able to kill half their number. That event would go down in history as La Noche Triste. Hernán Cortés survived the attack, he reorganized his army, and a year later crushed the Aztecs, bringing down their empire. This happened on August 13, 1521. Tenochtitlan was renamed Mexico City.

Bewitched

ERROR: Provoking a phenomena of mass hysteria directed against magic and witchcraft in most of early modern Europe.

When
1550-1775
In Spain until
1821

Who?
Ecclesiastical and civil tribunals across Europe. The lands included in the Holy Roman Empire were particularly brutal in their punishments.

Consequences
Accusations and trials led to more than 60,000 executions, mainly of women. In Germany alone, about 25,000 people were put to death.

It has recently come to our ears that in some parts of upper Germany . . . many persons of both sexes, heedless
of their own salvation and forsaking the catholic faith,
give themselves over to devils male and female, and by
their incantations, charms, and conjurings, and by other
abominable superstitions and sortileges, offences, crimes,
and misdeeds, ruin and cause to perish the offspring of
women, the foal of animals, the products of the earth, the
grapes of vines, and the fruits of trees, as well as men
and women, cattle and flocks and herds and animals of
every kind, vineyards also and orchards, meadows, pas-
tures, harvests, grains and other fruits of the earth.

Summis desideratis affectibus,
Pope Innocent VIII

The Inquisition was
established as a kind of
shadow government in
Catholic Europe with the
encouragement of the papacy
and the cooperation of
emperors and kings. Fear
became the order of the day;
in practice anyone could be
denounced for having entered
into a pact with the devil.

Pope Innocent VIII is known in history for his obsession
with witchcraft. His papal bull marked the beginning of

one of the darkest chapters in modern European history: the hunting, trials, torture, public condemnation and burning of thousands of people accused of pacts with the devil. The text that inspired much of the hysteria was the fearsome *Malleus Maleficarum* (*The Witches' Hammer*), written by two inquisitors, the Dominican monks Heinrich Kramer and Jacob Sprenger. It became a kind of macabre manual for the capture and murder of thousands of innocent people, especially elderly and socially disadvantaged women. Considered one of the most terrifying documents in human history, the text is subjective, irrational and very, very misogynistic. It considered women to be morally weak and easy prey for the devil and regales in quoting passages from the Old Testament to that effect: "I would rather live with a lion and a dragon than with an evil woman" (Sirach, 25). Many of those tried were healers, cooks or midwives. Generally, they were

The arrival of inquisitors in a town or village spelled trouble. They targeted women in particular, but anyone could fall victim to their accusations.

On trial by the Inquisition

Here is how the process worked:

• Indictment. People stood accused based on rumors or reports from neighbors. The accused had little or no rights. He or she was rarely allowed to present a defense against the charges.

• Detention. Often there were no prisons as such. Defendants were confined in rat-infested dungeons.

• Interrogation. By any and all means. As most of the accused were innocent, torture was needed to effect confessions. By using the rack, the wheel or thumbscrews, a mechanical device that slowly crushed nails and fingers, detainees were encouraged to confess. The rule of only using torture three times and then releasing the prisoner if no confession was obtained was rarely observed. The *Malleus Malificarum* recommended that torture be resumed if new evidence were submitted.

• Trials. If the prisoner were able to withstand torture, other means were used to uncover the truth. The most popular were:

• Trial by water. The accused was thrown into a pit filled with water. Those who sank were innocent. This resulted in most drowning.

• Trial by fire. The alleged witch was forced to walk on hot irons or reach into a fire.

• Confession.

And when the accused was finally brought to this point...

• Searching out accomplices. The confessed heretic was then forced under torture to betray his or her confederates. And so the grim proceedings continued.

• Conviction.

• Punishment. Witchcraft was punishable by death at the stake. Those shown pity were beheaded or had a sack of gunpowder tied around their necks, rather than being burned alive.

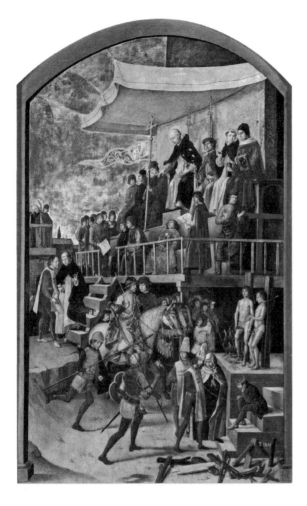

Places of execution were adorned with banners and offered seats for spectators. Terror was a popular diversion; the problem was that any of the spectators could star in a leading role the following day.

over 50 years old, single or widowed, and of low social class. They were to blame for all the misfortunes that hovered over the population: epidemics, plagues, fires, droughts. . . every misfortune was attributed to witchcraft.

Do not make a pact with the devil

40 percent of executions were carried out in the Holy Roman Empire (present-day Germany, Austria, Switzerland, Belgium, Netherlands, Luxembourg, Czech Republic and Slovenia). This collective madness lasted for centuries. The last accused witch was Anna Schnidenwind. She was sentenced to death by fire in Endingen am Kaiserstuhl (Germany) in 1775, over 300 hundred years after Pope Innocent's decree. The 63-year-old peasant woman was accused of making a pact with the devil and causing a fire in her town.

The Tribunal of the Holy Office of the Spanish Inquisition was also a relentless pursuer of the suspected witches. Founded by the Catholic monarchs in 1478, its mission was to locate, prosecute and convict those guilty of heresy. Tomás de Torquemada (1420–1498) was the first and most notable Inquisitor. He was personally responsible for the execution of thousands of heretics in the infamous auto-da-fé. The difference with the pontifical Inquisition is that in Spain the inquisitors were appointed by the king, and there could be no appeal to Rome. Torquemada's will was irrevocable. He held almost absolute power. Still, it seems that the punishments in Spain were not as bloodthirsty as those in Central Europe, and there were no massive burnings of heretics. In Spanish America, the Inquisition did not execute its judgments on Indians, as they were ignorant of dogma. However, the Inquisition tried to prevent the settlement of European Jews or Protestants in the colonies. There was an attempt to create a tribunal in Buenos Aires, but this was rejected by the Spanish crown. In 1808, Joseph Bonaparte, placed on the throne by his brother, abolished the Inquisition; but in 1814 Fernando VII returned from France, and reinstated it. It remained in a somewhat suspended state, until it was finally abolished in 1834.

This drawing shows Torquemada in ecstatic contemplation.

Is London Burning?

ERROR: The first was to allow the conditions that put the city at risk. The second was a series of decisions and hesitations that condemned much of London to the flames.

When?
September 2–5, 1666.

Who?
The baker, Thomas Farynor, and Sir Thomas Bloodworth, Lord Mayor of London.

Consequences
The fire burned down 13,000 houses, leaving 15 percent of the population homeless and razing a square mile of the city. It took half a century to rebuild London.

The conflagration was so universal, and the people so astonished, that, they hardly stirred to quench it; so that there was nothing heard, or seen, but crying out and lamentation, running about like distracted creatures, without at all attempting to save even their goods; such a strange consternation there was upon them, so as it burned both in breadth and length, the churches, public halls, Exchange, hospitals, monuments, and ornaments; leaping after a prodigious manner, from house to house, and street to street, at great distances one from the other. For the heat, with a long set of fair and warm weather, had even ignited the air, and prepared the materials to conceive the fire, which devoured, after an incredible manner, houses, furniture, and every thing.

Diary, *John Evelyn (eyewitness)*

Like the fire in Rome during the reign of the emperor Nero, the Great Fire of London cleared the way for the massive rebuilding of the city.

In 1666, London was one of the largest cities in Europe. In prior decades it had grown dramatically albeit in a haphazard fashion. A chronicler of the time, John Evelyn, referred to the city as "a congestion of wooden houses," a remark that points to the very real risk of fire. Enclosed within the old Roman walls, London was extremely overcrowded, with people jammed into a city of narrow streets, wooden houses and thatched roofs. It was a typical medieval city, where city planning was virtually unknown.

Hot cakes
In this disorderly network of

alleys full of people, worked the baker Thomas Farynor. His bakery, located in Pudding Lane near the Thames and the Tower of London, catered to King Charles II. In the early hours of Sunday, September 2, 1666, just as every other day, Farynor heated his oven to bake the morning's bread. The store caught fire by accident and the flames quickly spread. In the seventeenth century, the district where the financial district now stands was full of shops and warehouses holding flammable materials, such as oil, coal, wood and alcohol. The Farynor family was trapped on the top floor of the bakery. They all finally managed to escape the flames, except for their maid who was paralyzed with fear. She has gone down in history as the first victim of the Great Fire of London.

An incompetent mayor

The day began with high winds that fanned the flames. The fire spread to neighboring houses that had to be torn down or risk a domino effect. Of course, the owners did not want to lose their homes and vehemently resisted the proposed demolition. The only one with the power to order its execution was the mayor, Sir Thomas Bloodworth. By the time he arrived, the flames had already spread to the adjoining houses and were dangerously close to the warehouses along the river, which were filled with paper and other flammable materials. Firefighters were clamoring for the immediate demolition of neighboring houses, but the mayor refused. Many of the houses were rental properties, and he insisted that their owners be

contacted before any action could be taken. Samuel Pepys, president of the Royal Society and an eyewitness to the fire, wrote in his diary days later: "People do all the world over cry out of the simplicity of my Lord Mayor in generall; and more particularly in this business of the fire, laying it all upon him."

The king acts

The mayor's indecisiveness resulted in further destruction. By 7:00 A.M. at least 300 homes had burned down. The east wind carried the flames to the river, and by 11:00 A.M. the fire was unstoppable. It was at this point that Pepys sought out the king at court (located outside of London) to inform him of the magnitude of the disaster. He begged his majesty to order that the demolition proceed lest the fire devour the entire city. Realizing that the mayor was not going to take the necessary action, King Charles II sent Pepys back with the long-awaited order to begin the demolition. With him came the royal guards, under the command of the king's brother, James, Duke of York, to help in extinguishing the blaze. Upon arriving, Pepys met the mayor who was on the verge of a nervous breakdown, but still too proud to ask for help from the soldiers. Finally, King Charles II himself came to the scene. Seeing that the houses were still standing, he preempted the mayor's authority and ordered the immediate demolition of all houses on the west side of the fire.

An unstoppable conflagration

But by this time the fire was out of control and as the day wore on became a virulent firestorm. This phenomenon occurs when a large area burns, and the upper air becomes extremely hot and rises abruptly. The surrounding cold air rushes in to fill the vacuum and produces powerful winds. These serve to stoke the flames with ad-

Samuel Pepys could not hold back the spreading fire. London's mayor refused to give the order to demolish houses in its path. Pepys had to appeal directly to King Charles II before the necessary steps were taken to bring the flames under control.

Because London's streets were so narrow, little could be done to halt the fire until the wind changed direction.

ditional oxygen. The result is a firestorm that can reach temperatures above 2,000 C°! Wind turbulence then caused the fire to turn northwards, further spreading the devastation.

At dawn on Monday, September 3, the flames were heading north and west. By late afternoon, the fire had reached the wealthier districts, completely destroying buildings like the Royal Exchange and the opulent stores of Cheapside. People began to panic. There were rumors that the fire had been caused by the French and the Dutch (commercial rivals). Some immigrants became victims of lynching and street violence. Everyone tried to flee the city, but the narrow streets and high walls hampered their flight. Streams of people got caught up in stampedes trying to pass through the city's gates.

Tuesday dawned confirming people's worst fears. The flames reached St. Paul's Cathedral, destroyed it and engulfed the Roman wall in the area of Fleet Street. It was coming dangerously close to the king's court at Whitehall, when two factors intervened. Strong easterly winds brought temperatures down. At the same time the garrison of the Tower of London used gunpowder to create an effective firewall, finally stopping the relentless advance of the flames.

At that time, London did not have a municipal fire department. Until then, insurers employed their own fire prevention services. The fire fighters were equipped with rudimentary manual water pumps wholly unable to cope with large fires. It would take another 200 years to rectify the situation. It was not until 1866 that the first public fire department opened in the city.

Chaotic reconstruction

After several days of fire, the picture could hardly have been bleaker. The busy metropolis, which had been competing with the wealthy and powerful cities of the Netherlands, was almost completely burned. It had to be rebuilt to ease the economic crisis. London was still laid out as a medieval city.

The fire offered an excellent opportunity to start from scratch. The architect Christopher Wren, the architect of the rebuilt Cathedral of St. Paul, proposed a plan with long wide avenues and open plazas. But in the rush to return to normalcy construction proceeded without any overarching plan. Thus twenty-first century London still retains the disorganized character and corresponding charm of an earlier period.

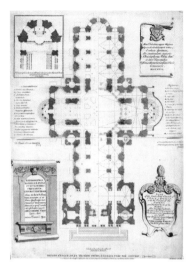

St. Paul's Cathedral burned down and had to be rebuilt.

The Monument

Londoners still remember that fateful September. The Monument to the Great Fire of London was designed by Christopher Wren. This column stands at the junction of Monument Street and Fish Street Hill. It is 202 feet tall and 202 feet away from the bakery on Pudding Lane where the fire started. Another monument, the Golden Boy of Pye Corner, marks the point near Smithfield where the fire was stopped. The Monument to the Great Fire carried inscriptions in Latin on its base describing various events and explanations. Its summary of the catastrophe says: "15 out of 26 boroughs were destroyed and another 8 seriously damaged; the fire consumed 400 streets, 13,200 houses, 89 churches (not including chapels), 4 large city gates, the town hall and many public buildings such as hospitals, schools and libraries."

I Need a Drink

ERROR: To pass a Constitutional amendment banning alcohol.

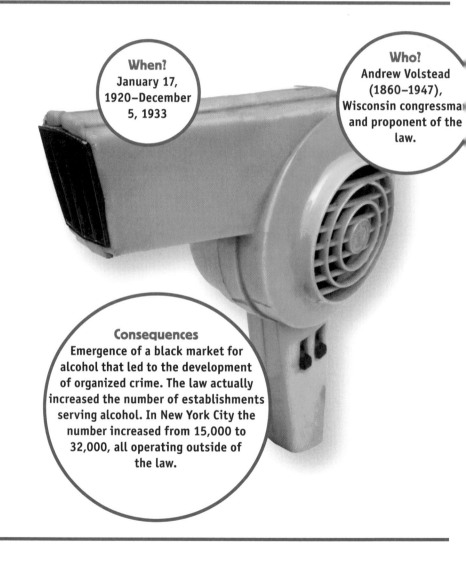

When?
January 17, 1920–December 5, 1933

Who?
Andrew Volstead (1860–1947), Wisconsin congressman and proponent of the law.

Consequences
Emergence of a black market for alcohol that led to the development of organized crime. The law actually increased the number of establishments serving alcohol. In New York City the number increased from 15,000 to 32,000, all operating outside of the law.

No person shall on or after the date when the eighteenth amendment to the Constitution of the United States goes into effect, manufacture, sell, barter, transport import, export, deliver, furnish or possess my intoxicating liquor except as authorized in this Act, and all the provisions of this Act shall be liberally construed to the end that the use of intoxicating liquor as a beverage may be prevented.

— *Volstead Act, Title II, Sec. 3*

In a photograph from 1921, police look on as workers empty a barrel of liquor.

On the night of January 17, 1920, an exultant Senator Andrew Volstead went on radio to announce passage of the eighteenth amendment to the Constitution and the enactment of Prohibition. The idea was simple: to prohibit the manufacture and sale of alcoholic beverages in the United States. One of prohibition's supporters, Senator Morris Shepherd, expressed the confidence of the dries (those pushing for Prohibition): "There is as much chance of repealing the Eighteenth Amendment as there is for a humming-bird to fly to the planet Mars with the Washington Monument tied to its tail."

Temperance triumphs

Immediately following the end of the First World War, American society was enjoying a particular euphoric moment. There were new music, new dances and a certain moral lax-

HALF GALLON

GENUINE KEG BEER

Hamm's

BEER ɪɴ JUGS

BOTTLED ʙʏ
BLUE EAGLE BEER COMPANY

MW: 46.06844   100 g

Alcohol

(ethanol, C₂H₅OH)

Handle with care!

ity in customs. Happy days indeed! Conservative ideas were temporarily suffering a setback, but that provoked a powerful reaction. With its flagrant disregard for the rights of citizens, the Volstead Act (the legislation implementing the Eighteenth Amendment) initiated one of the saddest chapters in the history of the United States: public censure of private behavior. The act did not stop with half measures: the manufacture and sale of alcohol were punishable by fines up to $1,000 (a fortune for that time), imprisonment up to five years and the closure of any premises where liquor was manufactured or sold. The only exceptions were for medical uses (which were strictly regulated), the use of wine for Mass, and cider. To enforce the National Prohibition Act a specific federal agency, the Bureau of Prohibition, was created in the Treasury Department. Its federal agents were known by the name of prohis.

For every law there is a loophole
Just six months after the ban, the Pharmaceutical Association reincorporated nine types of alcoholic beverages in its list of drugs to be used as sedatives and in the treatment of neurasthenia. In addition, about 15,000 doctors and nearly 60,000 pharmacy owners requested permission to prescribe and sell alcohol. This provided them with a windfall. In 1928 doctors provided receipts for 40 million dollars in alcohol sales. That figure reached 200 million in 1933.

Crime syndicates took notice and began to cater to this lucrative market. Crime Inc. (as the mob was then called) was founded just three years after the law went into effect. The first gangsters were Jewish (Dutch Schultz, Legs Diamond, Arnold Rothstein), then Irish, and finally the Italians moved in. They gained control of the business by extorting speakeasy

owners and bribing the police. The gangs controlled both marketing and distribution.

Al Capone, the legendary Chicago gangster.

Unintended Consequences

In 1925, there were 100,000 illegal bars (speakeasies) in major cities in the United States, protected by the mafia and the complicity of ordinary citizens. The new "Volstead nation" was becoming a real hell. Corruption reached the highest political levels. The Secretary of the Interior, Albert Fall, and Attorney General Harry Daugherty were convicted on bribery charges. The advocates for Prohibition had a lot to explain. They promised to end alcoholism, but consumption actually increased, and new patterns of drinking emerged. The cocktail became popular to mask alcohol, and the use of flasks became widespread. The intent was to put liquor producers out of business. Instead Prohibition further enriched them while decreasing tax revenues.

Prisons that were to have emp-

tied out became filled with criminals that the new law created. The 1920s saw 500 deaths from gang wars in Chicago alone. One of the most notorious bootleggers of that time, Al Capone, is said to have remarked:

They call Al Capone a bootlegger. Yes, it's bootlegging while it's on the trucks, but when your host at the club, in the locker room or on the Gold Coast hands it to you on a silver tray, it's hospitality. All I ever did was sell whiskey and beer to our best people. All I ever did was to supply a demand that was pretty popular. Public service is my motto. Ninety percent of the people of Cook County drink and gamble and my offense has been to furnish them with those amusements. My booze has been good and my games on the square.

Under FDR prohibition was repealed. Here celebrants drink from a case of champagne inscribed with his name from "Grateful Californians."

An ugly legacy

Finally, on March 4, 1933, the Democratic Party candidate, Franklin Delano Roosevelt (1882–1945) became president of the United States. In December of that year, Con-

gress passed the twenty-first amendment to the Constitution officially repealing Prohibition. Its legacy could not have been more disastrous: 30,000 people had died from ingesting ethyl alcohol; 100,000 people suffered permanent injuries such as blindness or paralysis. 270,000 people were sentenced for crimes related to alcohol sale and consumption, of whom one quarter were sentenced to prison and the rest fined. Homicides increased by 49 percent and robbery by 83 percent over the previous decade; more than 30 percent of law-enforcement agents were convicted of various crimes (extortion, theft, bribery or perjury).

FDR smoking with his trademark cigarette holder. As president he led the country out of the Great Depression.

Following repeal, the illegal sale of alcohol was no longer profitable. The mob, however, did not disappear. It simply went into other lines of business such as prostitution, gambling and finally drug trafficking. Currently, there are still countries where the sale and consumption of alcohol is forbidden, especially those with Muslim governments. In Saudi Arabia the production, import and consumption is prohibited; if you break the law you can be publicly whipped. In Kuwait you're put in jail, but not whipped. In Qatar you can be deported. Anyone traveling through the Islamic world knows that a stiff drink is hard to come by.

Hitler: Recipient of Nobel Peace Prize?

ERROR: Nomination of Adolph Hitler, Reichs-kanzler and Führer of Nazi Germany

---

When?
1939, the year he invaded Poland

Who?
Erik G.C. Brandt, member of the Swedish parliament.

Consequences
None. The nomination was withdrawn shortly before the commencement of the Second World War.

And so we National Socialists conscious-
ly draw a line beneath the foreign pol-
icy tendency of our pre-War period. We
take up where we broke off six hundred
years ago. We stop the endless German
movement to the south and west, and
turn our gaze toward the land in the
east. At long last we break of the colo-
nial and commercial policy of the pre-
War period and shift to the soil policy
of the future. If we speak of soil in Eu-
rope today, we can primarily have in
mind only Russia and her vassal border
states.

Mein Kampf,
Adolf Hitler

Totalitarian, anti-Semite, xenophobe,
warmonger. . . just a few positive adjectives used to describe one of the most despicable characters in the history of mankind. But we do not know what the Swedish
parliamentarian Erik G. C. Brandt was thinking in 1939
when he came up with the idea of nominating this bellicose political leader for the Nobel Peace Prize. In fact,
the Norwegian Nobel Committee (responsible for granting the award) seriously considered the nomination, but
thankfully, reason prevailed, and the prize was awarded
to the Nansen International Office for Refugees, which
was an organization dedicated to diverse social causes.

Alfred Nobel invented
dynamite to be used for
mining. He did not foresee
its military applications.
Having made a great deal of
money from this invention, he
instituted the Nobel Prize to
compensate the world for the
pain it had caused.

A "pacifist" looking for a fight

It is more than a little puzzling how one could have suggested Hitler for an award that is to be given to "the person who shall have done the most or the best work for
fraternity between nations, for the abolition or reduc-

It was a bit premature to nominate Hitler for the Nobel Peace Prize. One needs to recognize that many of the candidates have a long future in front of them in which they can demonstrate their worthiness.

tion of standing armies and for the holding and promotion of peace congresses." Brandt, who was responsible for the nomination, argued at the time that Hitler deserved the Nobel Peace Prize for his Munich peace agreement with Sir Arthur Neville Chamberlain in 1938. The idea is so outlandish that it had been kept secret for decades, not coming to light until recently.

By looking more closely at the famous meeting between Chamberlain and Hitler we can see how surreal the Swedish proposal really was. In the summer of 1938, Adolf Hitler insisted that western Czechoslovakia should by right belong to Germany, that it was in fact German Sudetenland. International tensions were high by the time Chamberlain and Hitler met on September 29. Also in attendance was the French Prime Minister, Edouard Daladier. Interestingly, the Czech government was not invited to the meeting. With an absence of foresight that has now entered the historical lexicon as the prime example of the appeasement of a tyrant, Chamberlain caved in, giving the Führer virtually everything he wanted; the Czechoslovakian government was required to immediately evacuate predominantly German regions. Germany annexed more than 16,000 square kilometers, which was inhabited by 3.5 million people, among whom were more than 700,000 Czechs. This historic mistake resulted in disastrous consequences for Europe. Why were the leaders of France and Britain so naive? Their posture was due in large part to the fear of provoking a global war (which ended up happening anyway) and, in all fairness, they really did believe that the sanctions laid upon Germany by the Treaty of Versailles had been excessive.

Before leaving Munich, Hitler and Chamberlain signed a document declaring their desire to ensure peace through consultation and dialogue. Chamberlain was gratefully received in London as a maker of "peace with honor, peace in our time." It was not known then what became quite clear later. Chamberlain's yielding only furthered Hitler's aggrandizing ambitions. Shortly after the famous meeting in Munich, the German Chancellor swallowed up what was left of a helpless Czechoslovakian state. And then on September 1, 1939, Hitler invaded Poland under the pretext of an alleged Polish attack on a German border post. England and France gave Germany two days to withdraw from Poland. Their demands were ignored, and World War II began.

Prime Minister Neville Chamberlain came back from meeting Hitler in Munich to announce that they had agreed to "peace in our time." He was later criticized for appeasing the German chancellor.

Josef Stalin was a mass murderer but a necessary ally to the Western Powers in the war against Nazi Germany.

Stalin *versus* Gandhi

Joseph Stalin (1878–1953) was also a candidate for the Nobel Peace Prize. He was praised for his efforts to end the Second World War, but in the end his candidacy was not seriously considered. According to records of the deliberations, former Norwegian Minister of Foreign Affairs Halvdan Koht nominated Stalin from a list of other world leaders, including Franklin D. Roosevelt, Winston

Churchill, Anthony Eden (British Foreign Secretary during World War II), Maxim Litvinov (Russian Ambassador to the United States), Edvard Benes (President of Czechoslovakia) and Jan Smuts (Prime Minister South Africa). Historians have attributed millions of deaths to the repressive Soviet leader, but in 1948 Stalin was nominated yet again for the Nobel Prize. In that year he shared the slate with no less a personage than Mahatma Gandhi (1869-1948). The leader of the peaceful revolution against British colonization died soon after his fifth nomination was once again rejected! As the Committee's rules do not permit the granting of posthumous awards this unforgivable oversight could not be rectified.

Mahatma Gandhi was nominated for the Nobel Peace Prize five times but was never awarded it.

Other ironies

The history of the Nobel Peace Prize is replete with errors. For example, the Committee awarded the prize jointly to Henry Kissinger, American Secretary of State, and the Vietnamese Le Duc Tho. They had held secret meetings in 1970 that led to the signing of the truce in Paris in 1973, and this resulted in the Prize. Kissinger was delighted, and then supported a military coup in Argentina, organized Operation Condor in Chile that overthrew its democratically elected president, bolstered the repressive Suharto regime in Indonesia, took part in the secret bombing of Laos and Cambodia, and never seemed to hesitate to engage in any operation that favored U.S. economic interests, despite what many historians have seen as war crimes. The organizer of the forces of Viet Minh had the decency not to accept his share of the Prize given the conditions in his country, while Kissinger joined the list of such Nobel Peace Prize luminaries as Desmond Tutu, the Dalai Lama, and Nelson Mandela.

Other Nobel Prize Winners

Since its inception in 1901, the Nobel Peace Prize has been awarded to 95 individuals and 20 organizations worldwide. In most cases the prize has been well deserved. Thus, the International Committee of the Red Cross, Amnesty International, Doctors without Borders and the office of the United Nations High Commissioner for Refugees have been recognized. The list of individual honorees includes: Albert Schweitzer in 1952; Martin Luther King in 1964; Mother Teresa of Calcutta in 1979; Lech Walesa in 1983; the Dalai Lama in 1989; Mikhail Gorbachev in 1990; Nelson Mandela in 1993; Kofi Annan in 2001, and Barack Obama in 2009.

The Great Leap Forward

ERROR: To launch an aggressive economic plan to industrialize an agrarian society in record time through forced collectivization.

When?
1958–1962.

Who?
Mao Zedong, Chairman of the Communist Party of China (1893–1976).

Consequences
His efforts to meet unreal industrial production quotas with an economy trying to recover from the disasters of war caused massive displacement of farmers and the greatest famine in recent history. Perhaps as many as 30 million people died from starvation in one of the greatest humanitarian disasters of all time.

One of the greatest debacles of the twentieth century began to take shape on a morning in September 1958 in the Chinese city of Hefei. That day, the first secretary of the local Communist Party showed Chairman Mao steel bars manufactured in the backyard of an artisan's foundry. This galvanized the Chinese leader. Finally, he had found the magic formula to transform agricultural China into an industrial power: reshape the Chinese peasantry into an industrial workforce. No more planting rice and raising goats, the future was in steel. Such a brilliant idea needed an equally inspiring name. And so the "Great Leap Forward" was coined. Mao visualized it all clearly. In fifteen years China would outpace British steel production. The Europeans would be left in the dust. The Chinese worker was unrivaled, and there were 650 million of them.

Chinese citizens holding aloft copies of Chairman Mao's Little Red Book, which contained 427 sayings designed to indoctrinate the workers and inspire them to create the New China according to Mao's vision. It had a print run of 6.5 million copies.

Mao Zedong was an optimistic revolutionary. He wanted to change the world. In the process he made a lot of mistakes, but his successors were able to learn from them and have turned China into an economic giant.

Paroxysm of productivity

Within months, Mao had constructed an extensive network of rudimentary steel mills in which legions of Chinese literally torn from their farmland were busy producing steel. Hundreds of thousands of cultivated acres were deserted. Moreover, as the manufacture of steel requires inordinate amounts of fuel, logging for timber caused one of the fastest massive deforestations that the planet has ever suffered. As aptly described by the author Harrison Salisbury in his biography of Mao, "Villages soon acquired the look of a place ravaged by a plague of iron-eating ants." During the years of the Great Leap Forward, tens of millions of people were mobilized to produce a single product: steel. An estimated 25,000 communes, or workshops, were created. This productive paroxysm reached such proportions that even factories, schools and hospitals were deprived of staff as qualified workers were forced to leave their normal work to devote part of their time to steel production.

Famine

The immediate results of such activities were not as expected. Poor planning and the excessive multiplication of local industries and workshops had the misfortune to coincide with long periods of drought and bad weather. The Great Leap Forward was anything but. In the early 60s, China suffered a severe economic crisis and food shortages due to the irrationality of abandoning farming for industrialization. Things became even worse. In the spring of 1961 China was gripped by massive starvation. Food stocks per capita plummeted to levels compa-

rable to India (three years before they had been 40 percent higher) and daily consumption was less than 1,800
calories. The government instituted an urgent campaign
of food rationing and about 20 million people whom the
Great Leap had moved to the cities returned to the fields.

China did not recover its previous levels of agricultural production until 1964. Along the way, millions of
Chinese were left dead by the enlightened thinking of
their leader. He finally acknowledged his error, apologiz-
ing for his lack of experience in economic issues. Cold
comfort for the millions of Chinese who must have wished
that he had arrived at that realization a little sooner.

Figurines of a group of
Communist leaders.

SCIENCE &
MEDICINE

42716

The Earth Is Flat

ERROR: Early Greek astronomers thought that the earth was shaped like a giant disk or cylinder that floated in either air or water.

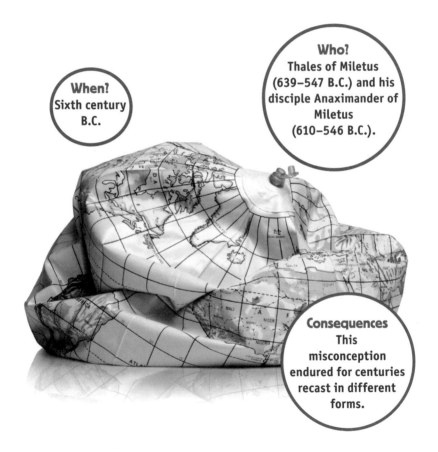

When?
Sixth century B.C.

Who?
Thales of Miletus (639–547 B.C.) and his disciple Anaximander of Miletus (610–546 B.C.).

Consequences
This misconception endured for centuries recast in different forms.

The earth's shape is curved, round, like a stone column.

Hippolytus on Anaximander

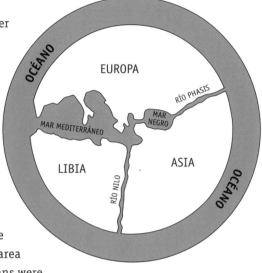

For centuries, man was convinced that he lived on a kind of round, flat disk floating pleasantly at sea. This idea goes back to Babylonian stargazers who produced the oldest known map in existence. This baked clay tablet is in the British Museum and represents the different regions of the earth with Babylon (naturally) in the center. The map shows a habitable area surrounded by ocean. The Babylonians were the first observers to develop an understanding of the planets.

The Greeks also thought the earth was flat but espoused various theories about its position in the heavens. The earliest pre-Socratic philosopher, Thales, thought that the sky was literally stuck to the earth (like a transparent snowball). The earth rotated every day dragging with it the stars, the sun and moon. Today, this cosmological vision may sound naive, but it was perhaps the first to dispense with mythical or supernatural explanations. One of Thales' most curious theories was about the origin of earthquakes. He argued that as the earth was a kind of giant, floating boat, the swell of the ocean itself occasionally caused earthquakes and floods.

Above: Representation of the world as seen by Anaximander. **Below: Shard** from a Babylonian tablet that contains a fragment of the oldest known map (now in the British Museum).

The **Garden of Eden** in a manuscript illustration from *Les Très Riches Heures du Duc de Berry* (fifteenth century).

A floating lozenge

One of Thales' most important disciples, Anaximander of Miletus, broke with his teacher concerning how the earth and heavens were related. He questioned whether it actually was freely floating in water, and was still somewhat confused about the shape of the globe. Anaximander theorized that the earth was a kind of oblong cylinder twice as wide (east-west) as long (north-south) and flat at the ends, like a kind of giant lozenge. He was not clear about the antipodes or if it was possible to reach them.

Considered one of the founders of present-day cartography, Anaximander designed one of the first terrestrial maps. According to the written references that are preserved, he pictured the world as divided into two equal parts, surrounded by ocean, corresponding to Europe and Asia. Hecataeus of Miletus (550–476 B.C.) worked along similar lines, drawing a map that provided new data on those areas that were most remote from the center of the world, which he located at Delphi.

Pythagoras has his say

Another thinker committed to demythologizing the stars was Anaxagoras (500–428 B.C.). He was the first to explain the phases of the moon and eclipses, which terrified his contemporaries. However, his theories provoked controversy, and he was arrested and imprisoned for his atheism. He had the temerity to say that the sun was not a god but an incandescent stone! Upon his release he moved to Athens, the new center of learning. But there things were no better.

There the theories of Pythagoras (582–507 B.C.) were widespread and astronomical phenomena were attributed to supernatural causes. Born on the Island of Samos, Pythagoras traveled to Egypt and Mesopotamia before returning to Greece to found his first school. The Pythagoreans applied mathematical ideas in their understanding of the cosmos, endowing numbers with a quasi-magical importance.

In one respect Pythagoras had it right. He asserted that the earth was round. He did not offer arguments to prove this contention. He simply regarded the sphere as a perfect geometric form, and thus Earth and other celestial bodies had to have this shape.

But the earth did not move; it stood at the center of the universe. The moon and sun revolved around it. The brightest stars were fixed in the sky, while the planets moved in space generating musical notes. This is the origin of the

Fragment of Ptolemy map dating from A.D. 150. There were many versions of this lopsided view of the world in circulation during the Middle Ages.

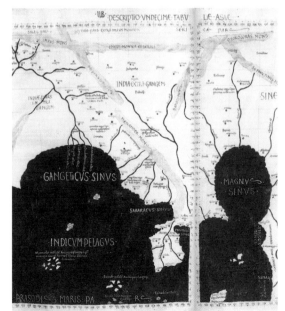

Above: **This world map** by the cartographer Al-Idrisi dates from the twelfth century. It was drawn from the accounts of Arab mariners. **Below: Medal** showing Aristotle.

concept of the music of the spheres.

Aristotle weighs in

We can thank Pythagoras for the application of mathematics to astronomy but still criticize his belief in the divinity of the heavenly bodies. This misconception gained further support from Plato (428–348 B.C.). Plato subordinated natural laws of the universe to divine principles. Celestial bodies were objects of worship. His most famous pupil, Aristotle (384–322 B.C.), continued to investigate the matter, displaying his characteristic intelligence in reference to the arguments for a spherical Earth. Here are some of his insights:

• Travelers who have come to Egypt and other southern places have seen stars not visible in Greece, and vice versa. This indicates that their horizon and ours are not parallel, which is only possible if the surface of the earth is curved. Although this effect would also be true for a flat surface if the stars were very close.

• The shadow of the earth on the moon in a lunar eclipse is always round, regardless of the day of the month and the height of the satellite above the horizon. If the shadow of an object is always round, regardless of the direction from which it is projected, this object must be a sphere. No discussion.

• When a boat approaches the coast, the first thing one sees is the top of the mast, and sailors first see the tops of mountains as they approach the coast. This indicates that the surface is convex. Since this is always the case the surface must be that of a sphere.

Geocentric to heliocentric

With the arrival of Theophrastus (372–287 B.C.), and later of Strato of Lampsacus (340–268 B.C.), we encounter the beginnings of the scientific method. It rejects divine first causes, espousing instead freedom of thought, observation and experimentation, in addition to the rational analysis of reality.

And so we come to a turning point in history. Upon his death, the empire built by Alexander the Great was divided into three parts. This heralded the decline of Athens, and the emergence of Alexandria as the center of culture and knowledge. Aristarchus of Samos (310–230 B.C.) was the first astronomer to propose the hypothesis of heliocentrism. It took courage to defend such "heresy." More than one defender of this theory has met a bad end. Case in point: Giordano Bruno, who was burned alive in Rome at the hands of the Inquisition 1,900 years after Aristarchus first suggested the idea. Another historical blunder.

Image of a geocentric universe. The earth is in the middle and the planets, the sun and stars revolve around it.

Some strange ideas

Anaximander of Miletus was not alone in offering theories. Here are some other ones that may seem a bit far-fetched:

• The world was formed when hot was separated from cold. Earth (Cold) is surrounded by a layer of fire and another layer formed of air. This layer shattered and this process produced the sun, moon and stars.

• The earth is suspended in the air, and nothing holds it up. It remains in place because of its equidistance from everything else.

• The first living beings were born in the water, with a hide of thorns. But in time they moved onto dry land and shed their thorny skins.

Who Says I'm Not the Center of the Universe?

ERROR: Defending the geocentric theory that stated that Earth is the center of the universe and the stars, sun and moon revolve around it.

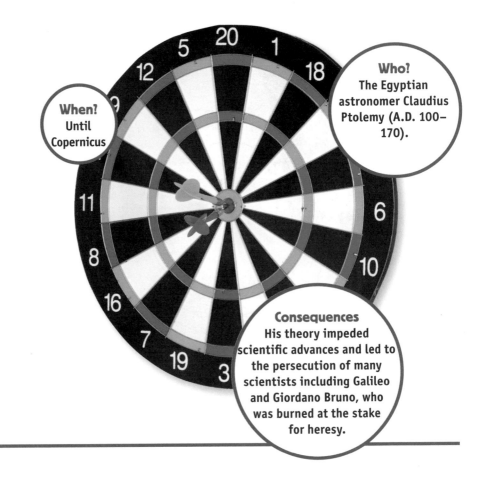

When?
Until Copernicus

Who?
The Egyptian astronomer Claudius Ptolemy (A.D. 100–170).

Consequences
His theory impeded scientific advances and led to the persecution of many scientists including Galileo and Giordano Bruno, who was burned at the stake for heresy.

In ancient times it was assumed that the earth was the center of the universe, period. This erroneous conception was propounded and defended by the great astronomers and scholars of the time such as the Greco-Egyptian sage Claudius Ptolemy. Ptolemy was an astronomer, chemist, geographer and mathematician and a tireless observer of the behavior of the stars. Ensconced in the legendary Library of Alexandria, he spent his entire life studying and cataloging stars, computing their brightness and magnitude and establishing rules to predict eclipses. . . But his most important (and mistaken) contribution was his model of the universe. Ptolemy was a geocentrist, that is, he believed that the earth was motionless and occupied the center of the universe. The sun, moon, planets and other stars revolved around it. His theory called for very complex movements of planets, called epicycles and deferents. Thus, the stars orbited the earth in a large circle (the deferent) while themselves turning in small circles (epicycles), moving them closer and farther away from Earth, thus explaining their apparent movements and differences in brightness.

Ptolemy claimed that the earth was situated at the center of the universe. All celestial bodies circled around it, propelled by the *primum mobile*, Aristotle's prime mover.

Question of circles

Whereas some seemed bent on establishing whether the earth was flat or round, others looked at the shape of the universe. Geocentric theories were very popular at the time. They continued to influence the thinking of astronomers and mathematicians until the six-

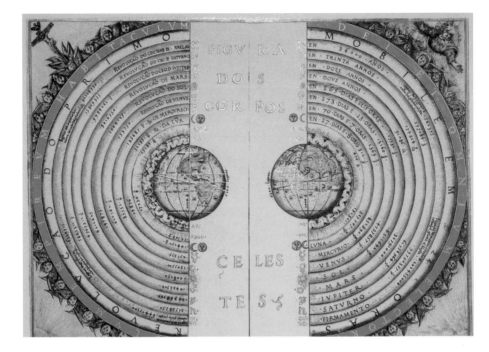

teenth century. Sometimes, humanity is a bit slow to realize its mistakes. . . Before Ptolemy, Aristotle had argued for the same geocentric model. According to his teacher Plato, Earth was a sphere that rested in the center of the universe. The stars and planets revolved around Earth in the following order (from the center outward): Moon, the Sun, Venus, Mercury, Mars, Jupiter, Saturn, and other stars. Ptolemy offered corrections to this schema. Earth, of course, remained in the center with the moon nearby. Then came Mercury, Venus, the Sun, Mars, Jupiter, Saturn and the other stars. But this theory had a problem that did not admit of an easy solution. The trajectories of some planets like Venus and especially Mars seemed to wander through the sky. That is, they sometimes seemed to be moving back and forth. This contradicted the idea that celestial bodies moved in perfect circles.

Aristarchus of Samos

For this reason some scholars began to question the geo-centric model. Earlier on the disciples of Pythagoras (such as Hicetas or Ecphantus) had speculated that Earth was one of several planets circling around a "central fire." Heraclides of Pontus supported the idea that Earth rotated on its axis, making one complete rotation each day. Some credit him as an early proponent of heliocentricism, but the evidence for this is weak.

But the most radical of all was Aristarchus of Samos. The Greek astronomer and mathematician has gone down in history for being the first to propose a heliocentric model of the solar system, placing the Sun, not Earth, at the center of the known universe. Archimedes describes a book written by Aristarchus that makes his case as follows:

Raphael's *School of Athens* painted in 1511 brings together all of the great minds of Classical Antiquity. Aristarchus is not included, but Ptolemy is shown on the right holding a globe.

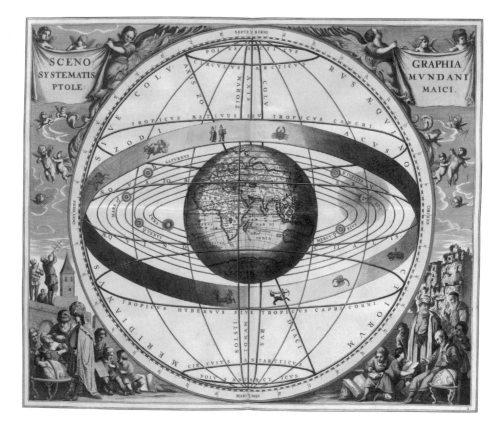

The German cartographer Andreas Cellarius published his *Harmonia Macrocosmica* in 1660, a celestial atlas that shows a view of the universe inspired by the discoveries of Tycho Brahe.

You (King Gelon) are aware the 'universe' is the name given by most astronomers to the sphere the center of which is the center of the Earth, while its radius is equal to the straight line between the center of the Sun and the center of the Earth. This is the common account as you have heard from astronomers. But Aristarchus has brought out a book consisting of certain hypotheses, wherein it appears, as a consequence of the assumptions made, that the universe is many times greater than the 'universe' just mentioned. His hypotheses are that the fixed stars and the Sun remain unmoved, that the Earth revolves about the Sun on the circumference of a circle, the Sun lying in the middle of the Floor, and that the sphere of the fixed stars, situated about the same center as the Sun, is so great that the circle in which he supposes the Earth to revolve bears such a proportion to the distance of the fixed stars as the center of the sphere bears to its surface.

Radical thinking indeed. Whatever could have motivated him to deny man the central place in the universe? His theory was greeted with bitter opposition.

All astronomers clamored against him, insisting that his argument was simple but wrong. If the earth revolved around the sun, there must be some variations in the relative positions of the stars, observable from different points of the earth's orbit. And that did not seem to happen. Of course, at that time astronomical observation instruments were too rudimentary to point to the correct solution: the earth revolves around the sun, but the stars are so far away that their displacement is too small to be seen by the naked eye. Moreover, they thought that if Earth spun on an axis, the winds generated at the surface would make the planet uninhabitable. According to Ptolemy, one could prove whether or not the earth was turning by dropping a stone from a tower. If that were the case the stone should land to the west of the tower (which did not happen).

Copernicus to Einstein

So the revolutionary astronomical ideas of Aristarchus were not well received. And things stayed like that for a long time! Displacing Earth from the center went against classical philosophy and Church doctrine, ac-

Copernicus was the first modern astronomer. He held so many jobs that he could only study the stars in his spare time. Nonetheless he radically altered our understanding of the universe.

Following upon the work of Copernicus, Johannes Kepler constructed a geometric model of celestial movements. Not having access to the data accumulated by Tycho Brahe, he could not fully grasp that the planetary orbits were elliptical, not circular.

cording to which the Earth must have a special role in relation to other celestial bodies and therefore its place should be in the center. It took more than 1,700 years before the scientist and astronomer Nicholas Copernicus (1473–1543) again raised the heliocentric model as a plausible alternative.

In his *De revolutionibus orbium coelestium*, Copernicus asserted that Earth and other planets rotated around the sun. But there was insufficient evidence to convince the skeptics. His heliocentric theory offered predictions of celestial movements similar to Ptolemy's geocentricism. There was no way of definitively correcting the geocentric error. That is until December 1610, when a man named Galileo Galilei (1564–1642) looked through a brand new telescope, which he had invented, and saw that Venus had phases like the Moon. Ptolemy must have turned over in his grave, because Galileo's observations were incompatible with his geocentric system.

Galileo also identified four of Jupiter's satellites, which proved that not all heavenly bodies orbited the Earth. All these observations were published in his works *The Starry Messenger* (1610) and *Dialogue Concerning the Two Chief World Systems* (1632). Only a year later, Galileo was forced to recant his ideas and copies of his works were publicly burned after being placed on the Catholic Church's List of Forbidden Books.

The debate did not end there. Another adherent of the new theory was Giordano Bruno (1548–1600). This Neapolitan religious and scientific thinker theorized that the universe was infinite and that neither man nor Earth occupied a privileged position in it. This blasphemy cost him dearly. He served a sentence of eight years in prison. Finally, on February 17, 1600 he was burned at stake for "tenacious and stubborn heresy."

Shortly after Bruno's death, the German mathematician and astronomer Johannes Kepler (1571–1630) formulated a model that described planetary orbits as elliptical rather than circular. He was followed by Isaac Newton (1643–1727), who in 1687 propounded his law of universal gravitation, which explained the shape of the orbit and the force that maintains them. And so on to Albert Einstein (1879–1955) who advanced his theory of relativity to revise our understanding of cosmology. For now, his theory is considered valid. But is it accurate? Time will tell...

Ptolemy vs. Copernicus

Is the earth or the sun at the center of the universe? It may seem an easy question to answer, but over the centuries it has caused more than one confrontation.

In his work *Almagest*, written between 138 and 161, Ptolemy makes the following assumptions:

• The sky is spherical in shape and has a rotating movement.
• The earth is spherical in shape and is located in the center of the sky.
• Because of its size and its distance from the fixed stars, the earth behaves against this area as if it were a point.

• The earth does not move.
• The planets move in small circles and in turn, orbit around the earth.

Centuries later, Copernicus wrote *De revolutionibus Orbium Coelestium* (1506–1531), which laid out his heliocentric theory. It argued that:

• The earth does not occupy the center of the universe.
• The only body that orbits the earth is the moon.
• The planets revolve around the sun.
• The earth is not at rest. Its rotation causes day and night.

A Sense of Humors

ERROR: To base the understanding of human anatomy on the observation of apes, pigs and other animals.

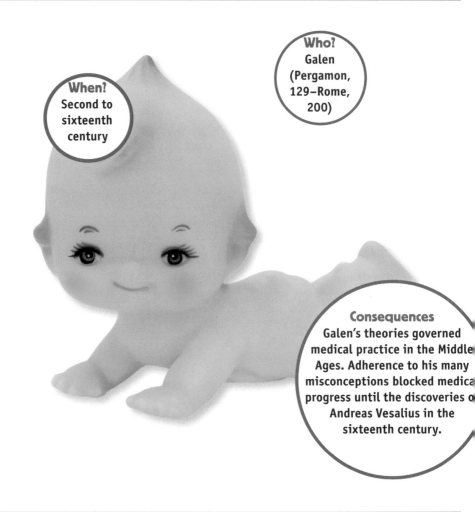

When?
Second to sixteenth century

Who?
Galen (Pergamon, 129–Rome, 200)

Consequences
Galen's theories governed medical practice in the Middle Ages. Adherence to his many misconceptions blocked medical progress until the discoveries of Andreas Vesalius in the sixteenth century.

For me it is clear, thanks to reestablished art of dissection and the diligent reading of Galen's works, which I have corrected in several places, that he never dissected a human body, was misled by his monkeys (whereas I did have access to two human corpses), and often fallaciously opposed ancient physicians educated in the art of dissection.

De Humani Corporis Fabrica,
Andreas Vesalius

Galen was born in the ancient Greek colony of Pergamon in Turkey, where at a very young age he began working as a doctor treating the gladiators of the city. At that time, these fighters (slaves for the most part) were highly prized. Keeping them healthy and fit was a heavy responsibility. These practitioners were not unlike the doctors that look after professional sports teams today. More than one gladiator was saved by Galen's treatments, and this increased his wealth and reputation. Success built on success, and he was sought out by the leading families of the city.

Galen gained his knowledge of human anatomy from dissecting animals, since dissecting human cadavers was forbidden.

Jean-Léon Gérôme, *Pollice Verso,* 1872. Translated from Latin, the title means "thumbs down," referring to the decision to spare or take the defeated gladiator's life. Among Galen's best patients were gladiators wounded in the arena.

ANDREÆ VESALII.

Andreas Vesalius provided evidence disproving most of Galen's theories. He taught classes in anatomy in Padua and received permission in 1539 to perform dissections on the corpses of executed criminals.

From Pergamon to Rome

Galen aspired to become the most important physician of his time. Pergamon was too much of a backwater for him, so at age 33 he went to Rome determined to realize his ambitions. Once there, he soon made a name for himself and became the personal physician of the emperors Marcus Aurelius, Commodus and Septimius Severus. Galen was intensely productive and prolific. Once his professional success was assured he began writing medical treatises. Over the course of his life he wrote more than 400 works, most of which were lost in a fire in Rome in 192. Texts such as *De anatomicis administrationibus*, *De usa partium* and *Methodus medendi* became medical dogma for more than 15 centuries until *Opera omnia*, a book by Andreas Vesalius, a Belgian doctor and anatomist, revealed Galen's many mistakes. For example, Vesalius found that the heart had four chambers, the liver two lobes and blood vessels began in the heart and not in the liver.

Some confusion

Considered one of the fathers of modern anatomy, Galen engaged in dissection of animals such as monkeys, pigs, and dogs. At that time, human dissection was forbidden. So it is understandable that his conclusions regarding human anatomy went a bit wide of the mark, since they were based on animal bones, organs and blood vessels.

One example was his description of the finger joints. According to his dissections of monkeys, he divided the hand into five tendons including the thumb. He overlooked the prehensile character of the thumb and its independent musculature, which is precisely what gives the human hand its most important abilities. Galen postulated morphology more suited to apes and other animals than humans. For example, this finest representative of Roman medicine considered pus to be a good sign, because it signified that the wound was being cleansed. This view persisted for centuries.

Nerves and spirits

Galen was also interested in the nervous system. After several observations, he concluded that all the nerves were of two kinds, one controlling the senses and the second physical actions (that is, sensory and motor pathways). What traveled along these pathways? Galen offered a hypothesis that would survive for 1,500 years. He theorized that because of its central position in the body, the brain controlled the other organs, particularly the voluntary muscles, through a network of holes that had "animal spirits" in them. To explain how these "spirits" were created, Galen argued that digested food was transferred from the intestine to the liver, where it was used to nourish "natural

Illustration from Johannes de Ketham, *Fasciculus Medicinae,* the first medical textbook to appear in print (1491).

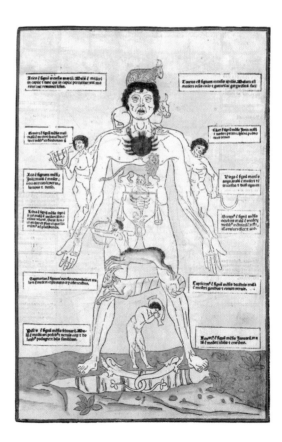

Mural from a church in Anagni, Italy showing Galen and Hippocrates.

spirits." The liver sent those spirits to the heart for conversion into "vital spirits;" in turn, they were carried by arterial blood to the brain and converted into "animal spirits." This was the first hypothesis to explain the phenomenon of the transmission of nerve impulses. Until the seventeenth century, Galen's hypothesis went unquestioned. The first observations with the microscope, which was invented in 1665 by Robert Hooke, showed it to be mistaken.

Everyone else is wrong

During all the years of his medical career, Galen refused to acknowledge any mistakes. His writings display an arrogant tone, regarding all those who called into question or contradicted his theories as unlearned, stupid or both.

Galen adopted the same strategy in debates. First he identified his opponent and summarized the opinion he was about to demolish, without missing the opportunity to label him absurd, feebleminded or worse; then he invoked his beloved Hippocrates and noted where his opponent deviated or even contradicted the sage of Cos.

Despite his many errors, his medical work had great merit, given that the instruments and means of observation of his time left much to be desired. In fact, modern human anatomy texts still use many of the names that Galen gave to certain parts of the body.

An engraving from Andreas Vesalius, *De humani corporis fabrica*, a work in six volumes on human anatomy.

The Four Humors

Galen subscribed to the Hippocratic theory of the four humors: blood, phlegm, yellow bile and black bile. According to this thesis, blood is formed in the liver; yellow bile in the gallbladder; black bile in the spleen; and phlegm, or mucus, in the pituitary gland. The four humors were fluids that correspond to the four elements and the four seasons: the blood belonged to the air and dominated in the spring (sanguine); yellow bile corresponded to fire and predominated in summer (choleric); black bile corresponded to land and prevailed in autumn (melancholic), and phlegm corresponded to water and was strongest in winter (phlegmatic).

Sickness arose from an imbalance of the humors. It was diagnosed by the pulse, urine and inflammation of the organs.

This May Hurt a Little (I)

ERROR: The practice of frequent and copious bloodletting to cure all types of diseases.

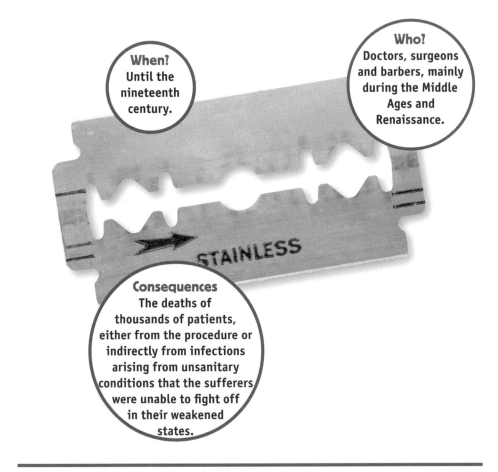

When?
Until the nineteenth century.

Who?
Doctors, surgeons and barbers, mainly during the Middle Ages and Renaissance.

STAINLESS

Consequences
The deaths of thousands of patients, either from the procedure or indirectly from infections arising from unsanitary conditions that the sufferers were unable to fight off in their weakened states.

Bleeding purges the body. It excites the nerves, improves mental and visual acuity and bowel movements. It provides sleep, cleans thought and expels sadness. Every day hearing, vigor and voice increase.

Medical Code of the School of Salerno (twelfth century)

Imagine going to the doctor for a simple case of the flu, and he decides to tackle the problem by taking a few liters of blood. . . Bleeding was one of the most widespread practices in the history of medicine. For centuries, doctors relied upon its supposed benefits, and it was commonly used until the nineteenth century. One doesn't have to go back too far. Benjamin Rush (1745–1813), an American physician and humanist, was regarded by his contemporaries as the "Hippocrates of the nation." He should go down in history as the "Prince of bleeding." Rush, one of the 56 signatories to the Declaration of Independence, believed that all diseases could be cured by bloodletting. He outdid himself during an epidemic of yellow fever. He performed more than one hundred bloodlettings per day. At first he pulled a pint of blood from his patients. But he began to observe that the more he pulled, the faster the recovery. So he increased the amount of blood drawn to over two liters: a statistic that makes one shudder considering that the human body contains about five liters in all. (Rush thought it contained eleven.)

Medical manuscript
illumination showing a patient being bled. It was supposed to weaken the strength of the illness. Oddly enough, some patients even survived.

Cleansing impurities

This unhealthy practice of bleeding the sick goes back to ancient Egypt. Later, Greek physicians like Hippocrates related bloodletting to the theory of humors. It was believed that diseases were the result of an imbalance of body fluids (humors). To restore this balance one had to induce vomiting, sweating and bleeding. Galen also recommended phlebotomy as a method of purifying the organism. During the first and second centuries, Greek physicians exported their ideas to Rome. There phlebotomy was practiced in *iatreion* (clinics), later called *medicatrina*. This procedure was intended to cleanse the body of impurities. It was used for cases as diverse as childbirth, pre- and postoperative treatment, inflammation, infectious disease, stroke and as a preventative of a long list of diseases.

A shave and a bleed

During the Middle Ages the practice was widespread. Monks would bleed themselves several times a year. Professional treatment came to rest in the hands of barbers, real bloodletting specialists. They would wash the heads and cut the hair and beards of their customers, but they also prepared plasters and poultices, extracted teeth, amputated limbs and bled their customers as well. During the thirteenth century, guilds of surgeon barbers were established to regulate training and apprenticeships, exercise social and professional control and establish codes of conduct for the emerging profession. Barbers advertised their services by placing a red and white pole in front of their places of business. The colored bands represented bloody bandages. Today, the poles can be seen in front of many barbershops. In the United States blue bands were added to pay homage to the national colors.

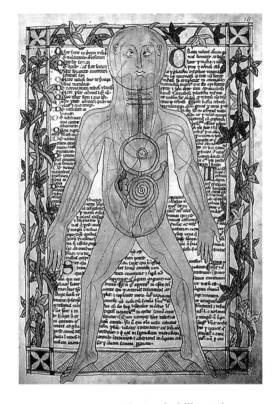

Anatomical illustration of the thirteenth century showing the circulatory system as it was understood at that time.

A risky practice

Bleeding was performed through incisions in different parts of the body. It was done with a lancet, a scalpel-like instrument, but with sharp edges on both sides. Holding it between thumb and forefinger, the surgeon incised a longitudinal or diagonal cut in a vein in the arm. Deeper cuts were also administered, using vinegar to increase bleeding. This often put the patient in danger of bleeding to death, which happened on many occasions.

Once the blood was removed, it was thoroughly examined. Diagnostic conclusions were reached on the basis of its look (and smell): whether it was thin, serous, foamy, oily, or gritty. If necessary, the same patient was bled repeatedly. A treatise published in 1557 affirmed that "blood is like water from a good source: the more you take, the more there is left." Neither children nor the elderly escaped the treatment.

One of its great defenders was Guy Patin, who held the position of dean of the Faculty of Medicine of Paris. In his considerable correspondence you can read about some his methods. He relates that on one occasion when his son was suffering from fever he bled him twenty times. . . According to Patin: "There is no remedy in the world that is responsible for as many miracles as bleeding. Ordinarily, our Parisians do little exercise, drink and eat a lot and become plethoric. Under these conditions, they will hardly be relieved of any disease, if they are not bled vigorously and copiously." During the seventeenth century, the practice of indiscriminate bloodletting was espoused by the most distinguished medical authorities, such as G. Riolano (1580–1657), Santorio Santorio (1561–1636) and J. B. Van Helmont (1577–1644). The French King Louis XIII (1601–1643) is said to have received 47 treatments in a single year. At that time, the common practice was to administer a monthly bleeding for adults and one every six months for the elderly.

In the Renaissance, it was common to perform bloodletting for infectious diseases. Thereafter the custom of bleeding patients near the source of the infection was introduced. In time leeches were used in cases of fever, applying as many as fifty to the patient's body.

Fortunately, this practice began to fall into disuse during the second half of the nineteenth century. The emergence of medical research describing the treatments and the results revealed that bleeding sick patients did not produce positive outcomes. It was also found that poor sanitation killed more people than the illnesses from infections. Unfortunately, many patients did not live to reap the benefits of the research.

The sick-making pharmacy

Throughout the centuries, science has tried to remedy all kinds of diseases using substances of various origins, be they mineral (such as lead, copper, gold or silver), vegetable (such as castor oil or wine), or animal (such as milk, fat, bones or viscera of animals). But over time, many doctors relied on a class of drugs made from such things as urine, menstrual blood, rotting flesh, pulverized insects, burned toads, crocodile dung, rancid grease and fly feces. In the medieval work *Pauperum Thesaurus*, Petrus Hispanicus recommended a cure for female genital bleeding: oral ingestion of goat manure mashed together with leeks and a poultice with horned frogs mixed with rabbit hair, manure and broth from cow heads cooked with worms.

A Snort a Day

ERROR: Popularization of cocaine as a therapeutic remedy.

When?
1880.

Who?
U.S. and European laboratories and the founder of psychoanalysis Sigmund Freud.

Consequences
Intoxication and addiction to the new drug.

[Cocaine] can supply the place of food, make the coward brave, the silent eloquent, free the victims of alcohol and opium habit from their bondage and as an anesthetic render the sufferer insensitive to pain

From a paper provided by the Parke, Davis Company

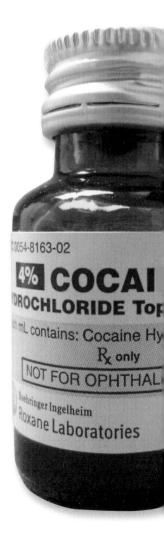

The coca plant is of great use in the Andes where one can reduce the effects of altitude sickness by chewing its leaves. Refined, it is a powerful stimulant that can easily be abused.

Our story begins in the sixteenth century when Francisco Pizarro (1476–1541) brought his conquering army to Peru. The conditions there were extremely harsh, and the soldiers were dropping like flies. After a while, the more observant among them noticed that the indigenous people were able to endure the most strenuous marches without any problems. They weren't supermen; their secret lay in the leaves of an easily cultivated bush that grew in woody areas in the Andes of Peru and Bolivia. While they chewed the plant over the course of the day, their saliva separated the powerful alkaloid that the plant contained, giving them the sensation of unflagging euphoria that the Spanish had observed. At this time natives could consume up to 50 leaves of coca every day. Spain tried to halt the custom by enacting laws and prohibitions, but to no avail.

The birth of cocaine

News of its effects eventually came to Europe. Returning to the old world, travelers brought leaves back with them and began to expatiate upon the properties of this magical plant. One of these was an Italian doctor Paolo Mantegazza (1831–1910), who upon returning from Peru claimed to have discovered a plant that when used carefully, demonstrated exceptional curative powers. In the same year the Viennese biochemist Albert Niemann (1834–1861) succeeded in isolating the famous alkaloid that was contained in coca leaves. Thus was cocaine born. Right away Americans and Europeans began to experiment with this substance, finding that it had many more benefits than disadvantages. In 1880 cocaine was included in the official list of drugs that constituted the pharmacopeia of the United States. Drug companies interested in selling cocaine, such as Parke, Davis, launched advertising campaigns to promote it. The association established to combat hay fever adopted cocaine as its official remedy. In short, there was widespread enthusiasm for this marvelous substance that fortified the nervous system, aided digestion, stimulated fatigued bodies and relieved pain.

Sigmund Freud saw cocaine as a panacea. When he realized his mistake, he did not hesitate to stop using it. Unfortunately, he could not do the same with tobacco and died from cancer.

Freud tries a line or two

In Europe the German scientist Theodor Aschenbrandt began to experiment with the drug, administering it in its pure form to Bavarian soldiers. The cadets were able to drill for hours without becoming tired and then sleep well at night. Aschenbrandt published an article that came to the attention of Sigmund Freud. Impressed, Freud began to experiment with the drug on himself to gauge its effects. The father of psychoanalysis became convinced of its benefits for digestive disorders, neurasthenia, facial neuralgia, asthma and even impotence. He also recommended it as a cure for morphine addiction. In this way he can be credited with creating the first cocaine addict. To cure the morphine addiction of his friend Dr. Ernst von Fleischl-Marxow he began to give him cocaine in small doses. The treatment did not work out so well. The patient died six years later, addicted to morphine and cocaine. Freud, however, remained convinced of cocaine's beneficial effects. He published papers promoting its use as noted below:

In 1884, a side interest made me have the Merck company supply me with an alkaloid quite little known at the time, to study its physiological effects. While engrossed in this research, the opportunity for me then occurred to make a trip to see my fiancée, whom I had not seen for almost two years. I then quickly completed my investigation on cocaine and, in the short text I published, I included the notice that other uses of the substance will soon be revealed too. At the same time, I made an insistent recommendation to my friend L. Konigstein, an eye doctor, to check on the extent to which the anesthetic qualities of cocaine might also be used with sore eyes.

In his writings Freud listed six areas for its therapeutic use: as a stimulant, for gastric disorders; for cachexia (bodily weakness due to prolonged illness); for alcoholism and morphine addiction; as a local anesthetic; and as an aphrodisiac.

Soon the drug's effects began to worry Freud's colleagues. In 1885 the German chemist Emil Erlenmeyer called cocaine the third scourge of humanity after alcohol and morphine. Other scientists joined in the condemnation, and Freud began to backtrack from his earlier claims. At the dawn of the twentieth century Freud established the bases of psychoanalysis with *The Interpretation of Dreams*. Its publication, and that of further controversial works, overshadowed his earlier adventures with cocaine.

Early on, Coca-Cola contained cocaine. It was, of course, a wonderfully stimulating beverage that its inventor sold in his own drug store. When production became industrialized, caffeine was substituted for cocaine.

Thank You for Smoking

ERROR: Convincing millions of Americans that smoking does not pose health risks with advertising campaigns that enlisted doctors and stars from Hollywood and sports.

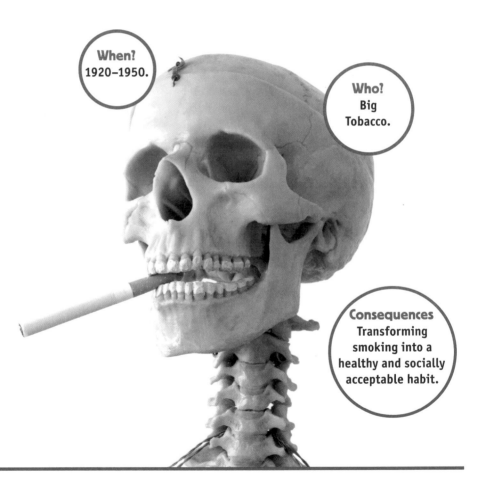

When?
1920–1950.

Who?
Big
Tobacco.

Consequences
Transforming
smoking into a
healthy and socially
acceptable habit.

More doctors prefer Camels.

Ad campaign from the 1950s

The world health organization has established May 31 as a smoke-free day. The campaign serves to remind people that tobacco is one of the most serious public health problems. Premature death, heart attacks, cancer and stroke: we now know all about it. But during the period 1922–1950 things were not quite so clear. Smoking was considered elegant, socially acceptable and even healthful for the throat, memory, digestion and to combat stress. This was shown over and over again in advertising slogans: "Take care of yourself, Smoke Chesterfields;" "L&M, just what the doctor ordered;" "20,679 Physicians say 'Luckies are less irritating.'" By the end of the 1950s things had gone so far that the Journal of the American Medical Association published a study demonstrating that Phillip Morris cigarettes were less irritating and suggested that doctors recommend them

to their patients. A few years later Marlboro launched a campaign showing babies with slogans such as "Gee mommy you sure enjoy your Marlboros." Camels had doctors pitch their brand:

Doctors in every branch of medicine — 113,597 in all — were queried in this nationwide study of cigarette preference. Three leading research organizations made the study. The gist of the query was — What cigarette do you smoke, Doctor? The brand named most was Camel! If you are a Camel smoker this preference among doctors will hardly surprise you. If you're not — well, try Camels now.

According to tobacco companies, cigarettes were recommended by doctors because of their calming effects. In time some of their less salubrious side effects were recognized.

Stars from sports and Hollywood

Among the benefits of smoking tobacco, companies touted the revitalizing effects of cigarettes. One way of doing this was to get the endorsement of famous sports stars. Joe Di Maggio, for example, became identified with Camels in campaigns such as these:

"I've smoked Camels for 8 years. They have the mildness that counts with me." Right off the bat, Joe Di Maggio, shown here at home, will tell you: "I find Camels easy on the throat — milder in every way. And they've got the flavor that hits the spot every time. You bet I like Camels."

Glamorous Hollywood stars were shown smoking in the movies, giving a tremendous boost to tobacco sales. Such images were bound to attract future smokers. Major studios such as Warner and Paramount entered into agreements with tobacco companies, especially for Lucky Strikes and Chesterfields. Clark Gable and Gary Cooper each received $150,000 to smoke Luckies. In popular magazines actors such as John Wayne, Rock Hudson and Ronald Reagan were used to promote certain brands. Even Santa Claus got into the act, posing for an ad holding a Lucky Strike. What was not advertised was that many of these stars died of cancer: Yul Brynner, John Wayne, Steve McQueen, among others. Humphrey Bogart was stricken by cancer of the esophagus but did not get medical treatment until it was too late.

This baby is happy to see his mother smoking. It is now clear that smoking during pregnancy or exposure to second-hand smoke in infancy can lead to all kinds of illnesses and deficiencies.

Santa lights up.

This May Hurt a Little (II)

ERROR: Popularization of frontal lobotomies as treatment for mental illness.

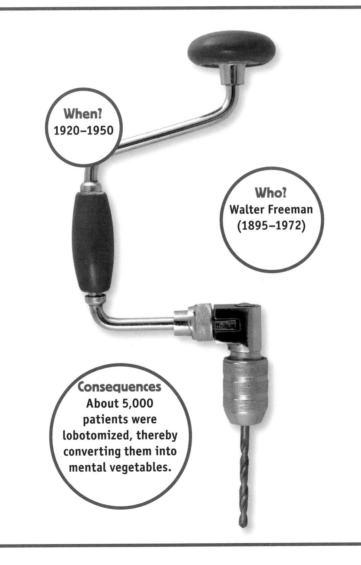

When?
1920–1950

Who?
Walter Freeman
(1895–1972)

Consequences
About 5,000 patients were lobotomized, thereby converting them into mental vegetables.

The treatment of mental illness through most of history has been characterized by truly abhorrent techniques. A case in point is trepanning, one of the oldest treatments for mental illness. Human remains have been discovered dating from the Neolithic Era that bear witness to this practice. Skulls more than 7,000 years old have been found neatly perforated. This "intervention" (for want of a better name) consisted in cutting and removing a round disk from the top of the skull to permit access to the interior of the cranial cavity. The procedure was often accompanied by magical and religious rites. It was indicated for wounds, skull fractures and infections, as well as convulsions and dementia. The Inca bored holes in the skull to allow evil spirits a way out and saw this as a cure for cranial lesions and nervous and mental disorders.

A number of pierced skulls have been found, leading archaeologists to surmise that some sort of cranial surgery was practiced in prehistoric times, perhaps to relieve migraine headaches.

Trepanning was widely used in the Middle Ages and Renaissance. But later on reputable physicians experimented with other dangerous and often fatal treatments, forcing patients to inhale carbon dioxide or sodium cyanide, or later using electroshock treatments.

A hair-raising technique

In the twentieth century modern surgical techniques for the treatment of mental illness owe much to Carlyle Jacobsen. This experimental psychologist described the effect of the destruction of the frontal lobes on chimpanzees. In one case a chimp named Becky who suffered from frequent violent attacks became as docile as Lassie after the removal of part of the frontal lobes of her brain. The

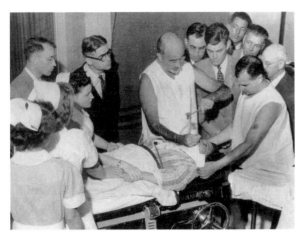

Walter Freeman lobotomizing a patient. The operation was performed through the patient's eyes. It involved literally wiping out a part of the brain.

experiment served to inspire the Portuguese psychiatrist and neurosurgeon, Egas Moniz, the inventor of the sad procedure of human prefrontal lobotomy. It was a high-risk operation, but it became widely practiced, especially in the United States in the first half of the twentieth century.

People with severe, chronic anxiety, depressives at high risk for suicide, and those suffering from obsessive-compulsive disorders were prime candidates for this treatment. Its main proponent in the United States was Walter Freeman, who was not even a surgeon. He was the inventor of a technique called "ice-pick lobotomy."

A metal pick was inserted into the corners of each eye and moved back and forth, thus severing the connections between the prefrontal cortex and the brain's frontal lobes. This method permitted the procedure to be performed without actually drilling into the brain. The icepick lobotomy could be performed in just a few minutes. Freeman was enthusiastic about its benefits. According to Freeman the procedure was so simple that it did not require special precautions against infections, nor did it have to be performed by a surgeon. Psychiatrists could do it in their own offices, and it would take no more than fifteen minutes. This idea that lobotomies could be performed anywhere, not necessarily in hospitals, antagonized some of Freeman's colleagues.

Between 1930 and 1950 lobotomies were performed

throughout the United States. Things reached the point where a van christened the "Lobotomobile" used to take subjects to motels where they were operated on. About 5,000 patients were lobotomized during this period with little or no follow-up studies to examine the efficacy of the treatment. The patients were mainly sufferers of neurosis, anxiety, depression and obsessive thinking. The technique was also used on schizophrenics and people suffering from chronic pain.

Most patients survived the operation, but its effects were dire. Lobotomies significantly altered patients' behavior. Critics insisted that the operations were surgical interventions designed to induce infancy and make patients more manageable.

Fortunately chlorpromazine (i.e. thorazine) appeared in 1954. It was discovered by the French scientists Pierre Deniker, Henri LeBoit and Jean Delay. The drug quickly demonstrated its effectiveness in controlling schizophrenia and other psychoses. It was found that the drug worked to calm patients without sedating them. Its use permitted many schizophrenics to moderate their most egregious symptoms and lead relatively normal lives.

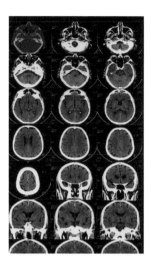

This practice flourished before it was possible to x-ray the interior of the brain, much less obtain a scan.

A Nobel Prize?

Ironically, Egas Moniz, the inventor of the precursor to this savage treatment, received the Nobel Prize for Medicine in 1949 along with the Swiss neurologist Walter Rudolf Hess, for the discovery of the therapeutic value of lobotomy for extreme cases of mental illness. At the same time groups of families of lobotomized patients lobbied that the prize be revoked.

The Tragedy of Thalidomide

ERROR: To sell the drug Thalidomide without adequate clinical trials.

When?
1958–1962.

Who?
German pharmaceutical company Chemie-Grünenthal.

Consequences
This sedative, which was administered to pregnant women to relax them and combat nausea, caused birth defects in thousands of infants, often leading to infant mortality.

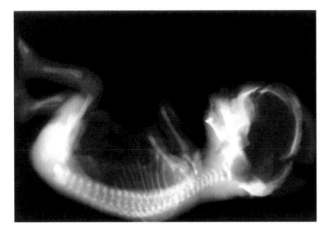

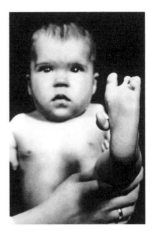

In 1958 the German pharmaceutical company Chemie-Grünenthal launched a new drug on the market, Thalidomide. It was advertised as the safest sedative available. It promised a peaceful night's sleep without any adverse side effects. In no time the drug was being sold throughout the world, recommended to children with sleep disorders and pregnant woman to counteract the nausea and vomiting characteristic of pregnancy.

At that time, there were rules and regulation governing medications, but testing for safety and efficacy was not required. There were only a few clinical studies of Thalidomide in Germany prior to its release, after which it was made available over the counter.

The sedative thalidomide was commercially available from 1958 to 1963. At first, it did not appear to have any adverse side effects. But then numerous cases of phocomelia (deformation of the extremities) were linked to the use of the drug.

A terrible legacy

Thalidomide was sold in 50 countries under 80 different names and produced more than 10,000 deformed children.

John F. Kennedy presenting the FDA inspector Frances Kelsey with the Distinguished Federal Civilian Service award. Because of her efforts, the sale of thalidomide was blocked in the U.S.

Blocked in the United States

Fortunately, the drug was never legally available in America. This was thanks to Frances Kelsey, a researcher for the Food and Drug Administration. Despite pressure from the manufacturer, she suspected that the earlier studies on the drug could not be relied upon and insisted that the drug be fully tested before receiving FDA approval.

Cases of phocomelia

Within a short period, Germany began to report the first cases of phocomelia, a rare disorder causing malformation of the limbs. In the first year 12 cases were reported, in 1960, 83 cases, and in the following year, 302. In Australia the physician William McBride noted that all of the mothers who had given birth to babies with phocomelia had used Thalidomide. He sent an article to the British medical journal, *The Lancet*, which declined to publish it, claiming that its methodology was inadequate. But cases of phocomelia kept occurring. Finally Chemie-Grünenthal withdrew the drug from the market, leading to its gradual disappearance in most countries where it was being sold. In Spain, for example, it was being wholesaled until 1963, and, according to the Association of the Victims of Thalidomide, it could be obtained for another four years after that from pharmacies' existing stocks.

Thalidomide has gone down in history as one of the drugs that has claimed the most victims in the shortest period of time. In only four years, between 1959 and 1963, the medication caused terrible deformities in infants around the world. At least 10,000 babies were born with birth defects. Among other anatomic anomalies were harelips and deformities of ears and eyes. It is believed that 40 percent of children whose mother had taken Thalidomide during pregnancy died in infancy due to serious internal deformities affecting their hearts, kidneys or other internal organs.

Better regulation

This catastrophic episode marked a new beginning in the regulation of pharmaceutical products. In 1962 Frances Kelsey was recognized by President Kennedy for keeping Thalidomide out of the U.S., and Congress approved the Kefauver-Harris Amendment, which required that drug companies provide proof of drugs' safety and effectiveness before receiving FDA approval. In its wake, further laws were passed mandating clinical trials, peer-reviewed methodologies, and no testing on human subjects without informed consent. Advertising was also subject to monitoring, and ads were required to include the risks associated with taking a particular drug along with its benefits. Inspections of manufacturing plants were required. In short the appalling tragedies brought on by Thalidomide led to a revolution in the manufacturing and marketing of drugs, and finally to a scientific process of drug approval.

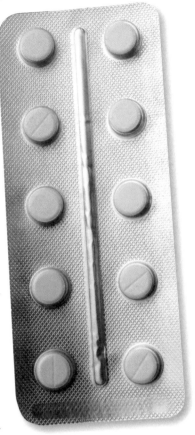

Today thalidomide is used to treat certain forms of cancer and some complications from leprosy.

Operation Ranch Hand

ERROR: Ordering the indiscriminate bombing of the jungles of South Vietnam with 80 million liters of Agent Orange, a devastating herbicidal defoliant.

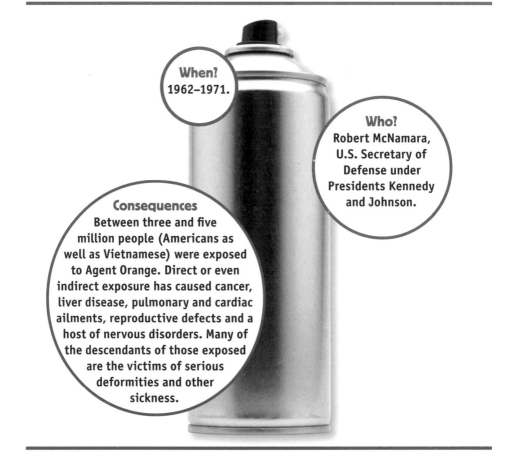

When?
1962–1971.

Who?
Robert McNamara, U.S. Secretary of Defense under Presidents Kennedy and Johnson.

Consequences
Between three and five million people (Americans as well as Vietnamese) were exposed to Agent Orange. Direct or even indirect exposure has caused cancer, liver disease, pulmonary and cardiac ailments, reproductive defects and a host of nervous disorders. Many of the descendants of those exposed are the victims of serious deformities and other sickness.

The war in Vietnam is going well and will succeed.

Robert McNamara

When the U.S. began its war in Vietnam no one could have imagined how disastrous an adventure it would become. As the war went from bad to worse, Secretary of Defense Robert McNamara came to a terrible decision. To combat the guerilla tactics of the enemy and their use of the jungle as protective cover, he approved techniques of chemical warfare. The method consisted of extensive bombing that eventually inundated ten percent of South Vietnam with herbicidal chemical defoliants.

Under the secret code name Operation Ranch Hand, the American Air Force sprayed Agent Orange (its name comes from the color of its containers), a powerful chemical agent with defoliating properties, over 25 million acres of jungle in South Vietnam over the course of four years. The herbicide covered the sprayed territory with an irritating toxic haze and a garlic-like odor.

A powerfully destructive agent

The effects of Agent Orange on the environment and human health were terrible. From an environmental point of view, it caused soil erosion, destruction of vegetation and wreaked havoc upon the indigenous animal life. The effects on the human population were similarly catastrophic. According to the Vietnamese government it killed thousands of people and was responsible for birth defects in as many as half a million newborns.

By the late 1960s a considerable backlash arose concerning its use. In 1967 more than 5,000 scientists petitioned the government to stop the use of herbicides

Robert McNamara, Secretary of Defense during the Vietnam War, made the decision to wage environmental warfare on the enemy. In so doing, he put the health of American soldiers at risk.

A plane flies over a tropical area dispersing chemical defoliants. Their effectiveness in Vietnam was somewhat lessened by the heavy jungle canopy. But if individuals came into contact with the chemicals or inhaled them, grave adverse effects could result.

in Vietnam. In 1969 a paper was published noting the extreme toxicity of 2,4,5-trichlorophenoxyacetic acid, one of the principal components of Agent Orange. Increasing pressure forced the Department of Defense to suspend its use in April of 1970. On February 12, 1972, the American military command in Vietnam announced that no further flights spraying herbicide would take place.

Lawsuits

Since 1979 groups of Vietnam veterans have launched class action suits against the major suppliers of Agent Orange: Dow Chemical, Monsanto and Diamond Shamrock. The first lawsuit was settled out of court with a payout of 180 million dollars. But the story does not end there. In 1991 the U.S. Congress passed the Agent Orange Act. It applied not only to Vietnam veterans but their families as well, for maladies associated with exposure to the chemical. The latest research has conclusively shown, despite repeated denials from the chemical companies, that exposure to Agent Orange can lead to four types of cancer: leukemia, soft tissue sarcoma, Hodgkin's lymphoma and non-Hodgkin's lymphoma.

Longlasting effects

But the worst effects have been felt by the Vietnamese. The inundation of the countryside with Agent Orange continues to contaminate its water and soil. The Canadian firm, Hatfield Consultants, analyzed the coastal zone around the city of Da Nang and found contaminants that were 400 times the acceptable levels. The mangrove swamps of the Mekong Delta, one of the most ecologically rich areas in the world, have still to fully recover their greenery. It has been over 30 years since the end of war, but Vietnamese people and their land still suffer from the effects of this campaign of chemical warfare.

With a Little Bit of Luck

ERROR: Rather than errors, these investigators attained glory thanks to a series of lucky coincidences.

When?
Modern times

Who?
H. C. Oersted,
Henry Becquerel,
Alexander Fleming,
Ian Osterloh.

Consequences
Important discoveries such as penicillin, electromagnetism and Viagra.

In the field of observation chance favors the prepared mind.

Louis Pasteur (1822-1895)

Once upon a time there were three princes who lived in Serendip, in present-day Sri Lanka. They all had the gift of accidentally making amazing discoveries...In honor of these legendary persons the English writer Horace Walpole coined the lovely word "serendipity." Since then it has been used to describe the process whereby one discovers something important by chance while looking for something entirely different.

There is no question that most scientific discoveries are characterized by a meticulous process of formal investigation. With the scientific method a hypothesis is established in advance and this dictates the precise form of the research that follows. And then the results will either prove or disprove one's original hypothesis. Up to this point, all is as it should be. It would seem that there is no room for chance in such a serious and methodical process. And yet, history is riddled with important discoveries that were unlooked for and came about purely by chance. Here are some of them.

The Dane Hans Christian Oersted discovered the existence of the magnetic field purely by chance. This paved the way for the development of electricity.

Electromagnetism

One afternoon in 1820, the Danish physicist H.C. Oersted (1777–1851) took part in a conference held in Copenhagen about the conversion of electricity into heat. By accident he left a compass next to a wire connected to a battery. When he turned the current on, he saw that the needle of the compass had changed direction. Further experiments served to demonstrate that the electric current produced a circular magnetic effect.

Radioactivity

Let's turn the calendar to 1896, when the physicist Henri Becquerel (1852–1908) stumbled upon the principle of radioactivity. While working with phosphorescence and photographic plates, he accidentally left uranium salt next to some of the plates. Their proximity resulted in clearly defined images, leading him to conclude that the penetrating radiation came from the uranium itself. This discovery, which came about entirely by chance, established that the nuclei of certain elements are capable of spontaneously emitting radiation which causes other elements to gain or lose electrons.

Henri Becquerel discovered the phenomenon of radioactivity after he accidently left a photographic plate next to some uranium.

Penicillin

Without doubt the most important chance discovery of modern times was that of penicillin. On September 28, 1928, the Scottish bacteriologist Alexander Fleming (1881–1955) was engaged in cultivating bacteria (*staphylococci*) in the basement of his laboratory in London's St. Mary's Hospital. Having just returned from vacation, Fleming noticed that one culture had been contaminated with a fungus and that the bacteria around the fungus had been destroyed, while the colonies further away were still growing. At which point he remarked, "That's funny!" Just by chance, before he had time to throw away the contaminated sample, he received a visit from an old colleague, who reminded him that it was in just this fashion that he had made an earlier breakthrough. He realized that it was a question of cell destruction. His immediate thought was that it was a substance from the contaminating mold. Right away, he isolated and cultivated the fungus in another dish. Finding that it belonged to the genus *Penicillium*, he baptized it *Penicillium notatum*. At first, the scientific community believed that the mold would only be useful for treating minor infections and ignored him.

With the onset of World War II the antibiotic drew the attention of American researchers, who were trying to find an alternative to sulfonamides, developed by the German military. The chemists Ernst B. Chain and Howard W. Florey developed a method for purifying the drug that led to synthesizing it for commercial distribution.

In a gesture of uncommon generosity, Fleming had not patented his discovery, believing that that would make it easier to access a drug that he believed would be beneficial for a wide variety of infections. His discovery changed the course of medicine and pharmacology and began the antibiotic revolution. Infections that once proved fatal could now be easily treated.

Penicillin has been crucial in the progress of medical specialties such as hematology and surgery, as well as in-

Monument to Sir Alexander Fleming who stumbled upon penicillin, the greatest medical advance of the twentieth century.

Staphylococcus aureus, was responsible for many illnesses, such as pneumonia, that would often prove fatal until the discovery of penicillin. Over time the bacteria has developed new resistant strains, and new antibiotics have had to be developed to combat them.

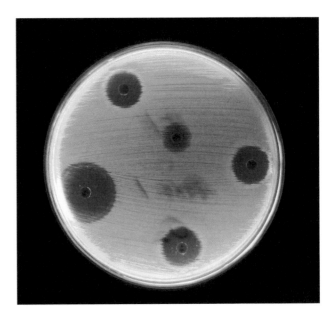

The famous little blue pill so popular among aging men and their grateful partners.

tensive care treatment. One of the most important results of the discovery, apart from its great therapeutic powers, was the beginning of a global investigation into microorganisms that have antibiotic properties, or are beneficial to human health in other ways.

Fleming was knighted in 1944 for his contributions to science and medicine. A year later he accepted the Nobel Prize in Medicine, along with Chain and Florey, for the discovery.

Viagra

This is a more recent serendipitous discovery. In 1995 a team of chemists, led by Ian Osterloh, and employed by the drug company Pfizer, was working with a pharmacological compound named sildenafil. It had originally been intended to be sold as a drug to reduce hypertension and combat angina. During testing Osterloh's team found that while it did reduce angina to some degree, its most pronounced effect was that it gave men erections. The investigation gathered momentum and within three years the FDA approved the now-famous little blue pill, Viagra, which has improved sexual relations for millions of men and their partners.

Researchers are currently pursuing a version of Viagra for women. In August of this year the FDA approved flibanserin, which increases sexual desire in women. It comes in a pink pill, complementing the male version. The manufacturer, Sprout Pharmaceuticals, has high hopes for its success, though some experts note that as female sexuality is quite complex, the cure for low libido in women is more likely to be found in their brains than in pill form.

Fishing expeditions

The list of discoveries happened upon by chance is very long, but of course you need to have the ability to see good luck when it comes your way. Apples fell on many heads before Isaac Newton's. In most cases investigators were looking for an explanation to related questions. It is similar to lawyers going on a fishing expedition when they know there is something there, but not exactly sure what. It takes preparation and being in the right place at the right time. Such has been the case with the discovery of champagne and cognac, vulcanized rubber, artificial sweeteners, X-rays, penicillin, the microwave and LSD. We can also add gamma ray bursts that led astronomers to infer the existence of the cosmic microwave background (not the same thing that is heating your popcorn) and who knows, maybe someday, extraterrestrial life.

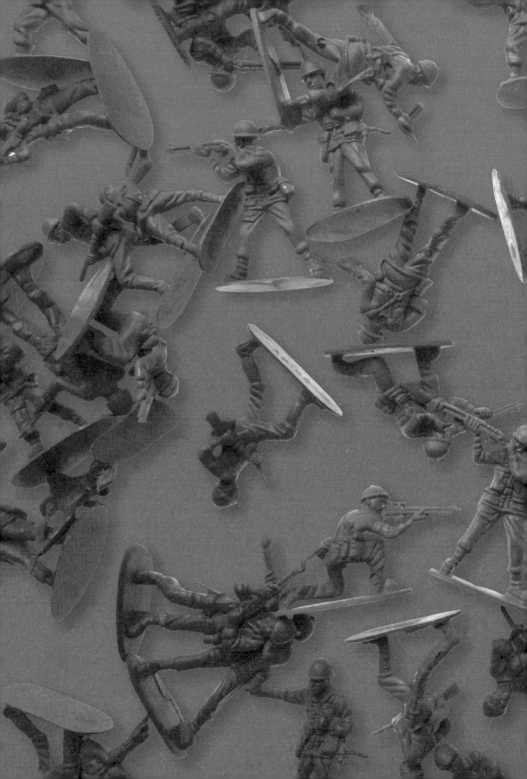

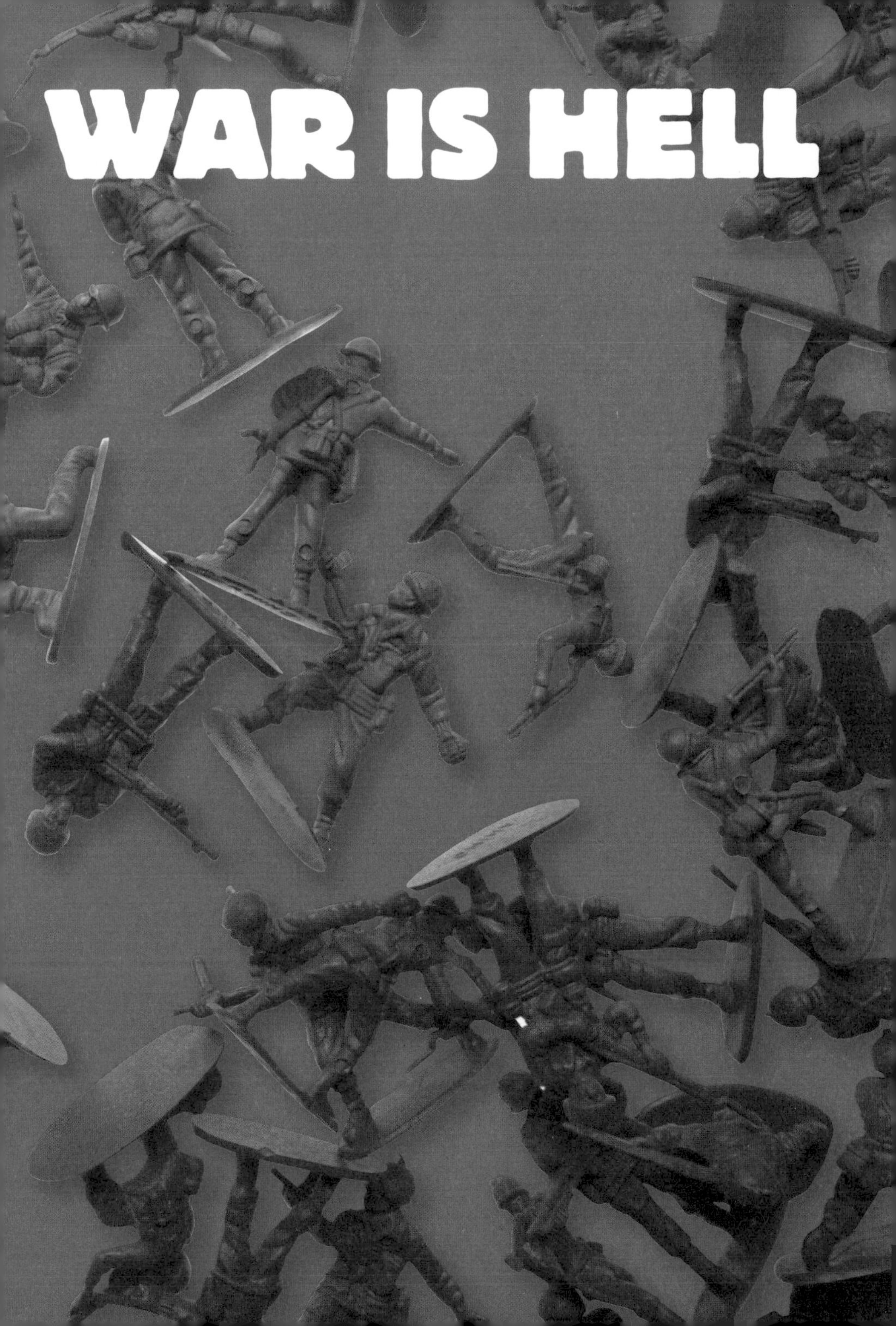
WAR IS HELL

A Superstitious General

ERROR: Ordering his army to retreat when faced with a lunar eclipse, as it was seen as a bad omen.

When?
413 B.C.

Who?
Nicias (470–413 B.C.), Athenian statesman and general.

Consequences
Loss of 50,000 Athenian lives and the end of Athenian dominance in Greece.

The fifth century B.C. was the Golden Age of Greece. It gave birth to new political forms, excelled in art, architecture and science and dominated the trade routes of the Mediterranean. The two centers of power were Athens and Sparta. The first had transformed itself into a great maritime power and, under the leadership of Pericles, aspired to control the whole of Greece. Sparta, however, resisted Athenian expansion. Over time the political and commercial interests of the two city-states diverged, and each established its own sphere of influence based upon alliances with neighboring states. Under their own leadership, the Athenians formed the Delian League, composed of the Aegean islands and Greek settlements on the coasts of Asia Minor. Meanwhile the Spartans allied with the powerful city-states of Corinth and Elis to form the Peloponnesian League. Greece was not big enough for both of them; hence the Peloponnesian War. The conflict lasted 27 years (431–404 B.C.), with some intervening truces.

The capture of Syracuse

The part of the conflict in which we are most interested occurred midway through the war in 415 B.C. In the course of the year Athenian generals sent a large expeditionary force (100 ships and 5,000 men) to attack the city of Syracuse on the island of Sicily that was fighting with Segesta, an Athenian ally.

The Sicilians were Dorians (as were the Spartans), whereas Athens and Segesta were Ionian. This division aside, Athens, under the direction of Alcibiades and then Nicias, wanted to conquer all of Sicily. Syracuse, which was the island's principal city, was not much smaller than Athens itself. To capture it would be no easy task.

As things turned it out the decision to make the

Alcibiades was the preeminent general of Athens. The attack on Sicily under the direction of Nicias proved an utter disaster.

attempt was an unfortunate one. As Thucydides reports in his *History of the Peloponnesian War*, the Athenian generals who conducted the campaign in Sicily did so with an insufficient understanding of Sicily and its population and so the forces that it mustered for the invasion were deplorably inadequate.

After they had disembarked and experienced their first engagement, the Athenians realized that this was going to be more difficult than they thought. The Syracusans mounted a fierce resistance, and winter was approaching. The Athenian army decided to retreat to Catania, which allowed Syracuse to recover its strength and get reinforcements from Sparta. For their part the Athenians sought help from the Etruscans and Carthaginians.

The struggle became more intense. Both sides constructed a series of strategically placed ramparts. The Athenians laid out their fortifications in a circle hoping to isolate Syracuse from the rest of the island, and the Syracusans countered with well-manned fortifications of their own. The Athenians, however, were able to gain the advantage and completely encircled the city. Increasingly desperate, the Syracusans set into motion negotiations with Nicias. But at the same time reinforcements from Sparta were arriving. First to land was the Spartan general Gylippus at the head of a large army. Arriving in Italy he supplemented his forces with recruits from various Sicilian cities and succeeded in breaking the siege of Syracuse, having defeated the Athenians in a series of battles.

Pallas Athena was not a lot of help to Athens in this instance. The city-state, sure of its power, embarked upon an extremely costly military adventure. Because of the poor execution of the invasion, Sparta won the battle to take Sicily.

Very superstitious

In July of 413 the Athenian generals Demosthenes and Eurymedon landed in Sicily with 73 triremes and 15,000 men. Before them lay a Dantesque panorama. There was swampland all around and many of the soldiers were sick, including Nicias. Demosthenes assumed command of the Athenian forces and engaged the enemy in a few battles. But the Athenians were in bad shape. Despite their wounded pride — mighty Athens was unable to defeat puny Syracuse — the decision was reached to call off the invasion and return home. But Nicias would have none of it. He refused to return home to Athens defeated. In the end, the other commanders managed to convince him that it was best to leave before things got really ugly. The troops readied themselves to depart, when Nicias allowed superstition to change his mind. That very night there was a lunar eclipse. Seeing it as a bad omen, Nicias decided to postpone the withdrawal of the army "three times nine days" on the advice of his soothsayers. That gave the Spartans long enough to block the entire port of Syracuse.

In an attempt born of desperation, on September 10 the Athenians made a beeline for the harbor. The battle was chaotic given the tight quarters and quantity of ships. In the end the Syracusan victory was decisive. Thousands of Athenians died on account of their general's superstitious nature. An additional 7,000 prisoners, condemned to forced labor, died within a few months due to sickness and harsh conditions.

Athenian soldiers were able to compete with the Spartans in strength and ability. In Sicily the Athenians sought to increase their power; the Spartans wanted only to weaken their rival.

This historic defeat was the beginning of the end for Athens. The Peloponnesian War completely changed the balance of power. Athens no longer reigned supreme. A newly invigorated Sparta became the major power in Greece.

Russia? Not a Problem

ERROR: Setting out with 600,000 troops to conquer Russia without taking into account the difficulties of terrain, the adverse effects of climate and the spirit of resistance of the Russian people.

When?
Autumn–
winter
1812.

Who?
Napoleon
Bonaparte
(1769-1821).

Consequences
Napoleon's military adventure cost the lives of 400,000 men, 200,000 from the French army and 200,000 Russians. An additional 150,000 French soldiers were taken prisoner.

History is the version of past events that people have decided to agree upon.
                    Napoleon Bonaparte

At the beginning of the nineteenth century there were two great emperors in Europe: Napoleon Bonaparte in the West and Alexander I, Tsar of Russia, in the East. Although each was wary of the other, conflict seemed unavoidable. Friction between the two powers reached such a point that a continental blockade was close to ruining Russia, and the French-Austrian alliance was endangered. But the final precipitant of Napoleon's invasion was Russian concern over Poland, which the French had carved out of the Austro-Hungarian Empire.

This famous portrait of Napoleon by Jacques-Louis David shows him crossing the St. Bernard Pass in the Alps. He assembled an army of 600,000 men for his invasion of Russia.

An extremely difficult task

On April 8, 1812, the Tsar demanded that Napoleon keep his troops on the western side of the Elbe. Far from complying with this demand, Napoleon gathered together a formidable army and crossed the Niemen River at the end of June.

Napoleon was in command of 600,000 troops, known as La Grande Armée. Most of the soldiers came from France, Belgium and Holland. Backed by such a vast military force, Napoleon felt confident that he could accomplish his ambitious task: the conquest of Tsarist Russia. Accordingly, in May of 1812, the largest European army ever assembled began preparations for the march on Moscow. The intervening territories raised no difficulties;

both the kings of Saxony and Prussia and the Emperor of Austria allowed Napoleon's troops free passage. They all stood bareheaded before the French conqueror with his two-cornered hat.

The Napoleonic colossus encountered no resistance in its initial advance. The French troops were far superior to their Russian counterparts both in numbers and in expertise. The emperor's campaign was going just as he anticipated. He belittled the Russian army and its generals. He took Vilnius and occupied Vitebsk, but his main objective was to lure the Russian army into open battle.

Approach of "General Winter"

To the exasperation of the French leader, the Russian army continued to avoid confrontations with the enemy. The Russians knew that they could not defeat Napoleon's army in battle. So they kept retreating, drawing the French ever deeper into Russian territory. Days, weeks, even months were spent playing this interminable game of cat and mouse. Finally "General Winter" arrived, threatening the gigantic army with the cold and a dearth of provisions.

Time was not on the French side. The army grew weaker by the day. Fed up with Russian tactics Napoleon led his troops into Moscow, thinking he could pressure Alexander into a negotiated settlement. No such luck. Upon entering the capital, the French realized that they had been lured into a trap. They were the conquerors of a deserted city. Most of its buildings were made of wood, and these had been abandoned and set ablaze by their retreating inhabitants, effectively denying the French troops shelter and

Arriving in Moscow, the French found the city set on fire by its vanished population. Left without provisions and faced with the onset of winter, Napoleon had no choice but to order his forces to retreat.

destroying any stocks with which they could reprovision themselves. Napoleon's army was completely isolated in a city that had been reduced to ashes. Furthermore, its western supply routes were easily cut off by the relatively intact Russian forces.

A bitterly cold retreat

Forced to swallow his pride, Napoleon ordered the retreat from Moscow on October 19, launching one of history's most famous military debacles. During its grueling march west, the French army was continually harried by the cavalry attacks of the Cossacks and ambushes from the Russian peasantry. Supplying such a large body of men became increasingly difficult. The rate of desertion skyrocketed while men and horses succumbed to hunger, exposure and exhaustion.

Recently it was discovered that another terrible enemy was assailing the French army. French scientists from the National Center for Scientific Research, working in 1995, analyzed the DNA of 72 teeth taken from the skeletons of 35 soldiers in a mass military grave in Vilnius (in present-day Lithuania). After performing batteries of tests they determined that the unsanitary conditions plaguing the retreating French army, combined with hunger and exposure to the cold, had caused massive outbreaks of infections brought on by the ubiquitous presence of lice and fleas. Typhoid and trench fever quickly appeared, cruelly decimating the emperor's exhausted army.

Of the 600,000 soldiers that had marched into Russia only 200,000 sick, hungry men returned to their homes. Napoleon's disastrous Russian campaign put paid to his ambitions to conquer all of Europe and heralded his defeat at Waterloo and eventual exile to the island of Saint Helena.

Napoleon never changed.
Even when he was imprisoned on the Island of St. Helena, he still dreamed of returning to France and raising a new conquering army.

Waterloo

ERROR: Tactical errors on the part of Napoleon's generals and Napoleon's overreaching led to total French defeat at the hands of the British and Prussians.

When?
June 18, 1815.

Who?
Napolen Bonaparte (1769-1821).

Consequences
The French defeat and the death of 40,000 soldiers on the battlefield resulted in Napoleon's abdication, restoration of the French monarchy and a redrawn map of Europe.

Two years after Napoleon's disastrous Russian campaign, a coalition of Prussian, Austrian and Russian forces captured Paris and forced his abdication. The emperor was exiled to the island of Elba. There he was quite comfortable but was dying of boredom. He spent his time studying maps, dining well and enjoying the hospitality of the port city that was proud to welcome such an honored guest. His English captors relaxed their watch over him. A high British official was charged with overseeing the detainment, but the prisoner was able to influence his guards and make them his own. Fed up with the contemplative life, he launched a small boat and escaped to the mainland on February 26, 1815. Within a week he was back in Paris, where he was welcomed with open arms. He was able to regain his throne without firing a single shot. He brought together all the officers of La Grande Armée. Napoleon's return signaled the beginning of what historians call "The Hundred Days."

Jean-Auguste-Dominique Ingres, *Napoleon on His Imperial Throne* (1806). This idealized portrait shows the emperor in all of his splendor.

A new coalition of European powers — Austria, Russia, Great Britain and Prussia — assembled in the Netherlands to oppose the Emperor. Napoleon had no desire for allies. With an army of 125,000 he set out right away for Brussels, aiming to recoup some of his lost territory. It was there that the British under the Duke of Wellington and the Prussian army lead by General von Blücher sought to check his advance. The emperor himself was not well, suffering from hemorrhoids that pre-

Arthur Wellesley, first Duke of Wellington in this portrait by Goya, was named a grandee of Spain, not only for Waterloo, but also for his brilliant victories during the Peninsular War.

vented him from spending much time on horseback.

Defeat at Waterloo

On October 15, 1815 the French troops arrived in position for the attack. Napoleon ordered 60,000 troops to fall back to Wavre after his army had engaged with the Prussians at the Battle of Ligny. At the same time Napoleon's battlefield commander, Marshal Ney, headed toward Brussels where he encountered Wellington's forces at the Battle of Quatre Bras.

Things were going badly for the coalition forces, and Wellington had them retreat to Waterloo. Ney's army followed on his left flank. Napoleon felt that the time had arrived to finally crush the British forces.

At 11:30 A.M. (Napoleon did not like to get up early) on June 18 the final battle began in an open field about a mile outside of Waterloo (in present-day Belgium). On one side were 70,000 French, on the other 140,000, mainly Prussians and British.

Aware of his relative weakness in numbers, Napoleon tried to draw off the Prussian troops by launching an artillery attack on the fortified Chateau Hougoumont. But Wellington divined his opponent's intentions and called for a full-scale frontal assault on the French line.

Around 1:00 in the afternoon, Blücher's troops began

to arrive from the east, entering the battle three hours later and forcing Napoleon's army to retreat. At 6:00 Ney's troops launched a counterattack at the center of Wellington's line but were repulsed by Wellington's forces. The French army was weakening, and then Prussian soldiers attacked the rear from a place of concealment. That tipped the balance. By 9:00 that night Wellington and Blücher met up at La Belle Alliance, an inn nearby Napoleon's headquarters. The Battle of Waterloo ended in the complete defeat of the French.

A month later, on July 15, British authorities accepted Napoleon's resignation. The former emperor was sent into exile again, this time to an isolated island in the Atlantic, Saint Helena, where he died seven years later.

Adolf Northern, *Prussian Attack at Waterloo.* The action took place at Plancenoit.

English engraving makes fun of the great French emperor after his defeat and exile.

One for the Indians

ERROR: To underestimate the Sioux Nation and think that one regiment could defeat a much more numerous foe in unfamiliar territory.

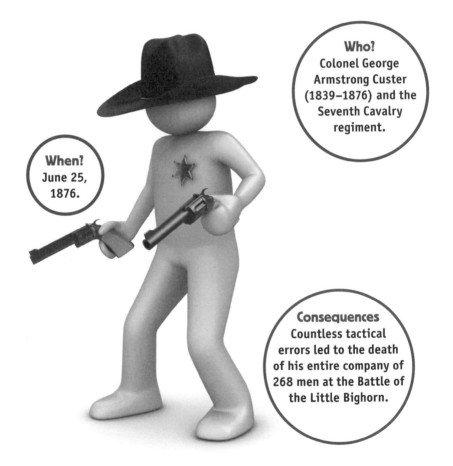

Who?
Colonel George Armstrong Custer (1839–1876) and the Seventh Cavalry regiment.

When?
June 25, 1876.

Consequences
Countless tactical errors led to the death of his entire company of 268 men at the Battle of the Little Bighorn.

*There are not enough Indians in the
world to defeat the Seventh Cavalry.*
George Armstrong Custer

The story of Colonel George Custer
depends on whom you listen to: his
friends or his detractors. According
to the first he was a heroic and valiant soldier who gave his life for
his country. His critics, on the other
hand, view him as a proud and
boastful officer who was willing to
sacrifice the men under his command for the sake of his own self-
aggrandizement. It's probably best
to let the facts speak for themselves.

Upon the conclusion of the
American Revolution (1784) many
of the citizens of the new country

George Armstrong Custer
had a reputation as a fine
military commander until the
Battle of Little Bighorn.

decided to move to the open lands west of the Appala-
chian Mountains. But in order to do so they had to con-
tend with the indigenous population of Native Americans
that was not at all disposed to share their lands with the
encroaching "palefaces." The settlers saw only two solu-
tions to the so-called Indian question: either domesti-
cate them and have them become farmers, or herd them
into confined districts, forcing them into reservations.

It is not surprising that the Sioux, a nation of warriors, relished neither of the alternatives. They were here
first, and there was no way they were about to abandon
the land of their ancestors. War seemed the only way of
the resolving the differences. It did not help the cause
of peace that the two main leaders of the Sioux were Sitting Bull (1831–1890) and Crazy Horse (1840–1877), both

courageous fighters who did not hesitate to attack anyone who attempted to settle in their territory.

There's gold in those hills

Tension increased. The Northern Pacific railroad had to suspend operations due to constant Indian raids. Things became even more complicated when the rumor began to circulate that there was gold in the Black Hills of Dakota Territory. But these mountains were sacred to the Sioux, and it had been agreed that no white man would set foot there. In 1874 the government sent men to investigate whether there was any truth to the rumor of gold. Command of the investigative team was given to Custer at the head of the Seventh Cavalry. For reasons that are hard to fathom Custer reported that the area was abounding in gold. Not surprisingly this ignited gold fever in the Sioux's sacred grounds. The hills were inundated with an influx of would-be miners who sought concessions from the government on every hand. As might have been expected, several tribes of Plains Indians formed an alliance inspired by Sitting Bull. Crazy Horse was in charge of the army of braves. Attacks on the intruders became a daily occurrence: first on the settlers and then on the soldiers who were there to defend them.

The government's response was predictably naïve. President Grant, whose first campaign slogan was "Let us have peace," referring both to the post-Civil-War South and to the western Indian tribes, came to revise his policy:

President Ulysses S. Grant responded to popular opinion. The Indians had to be suppressed. They were attacking white settlers, and there was gold in the mountains of their sacred lands.

> *The building of railroads and the access thereby given to all the agricultural and mineral regions of the country is rapidly bringing civilized settlements into contact with all the tribes of indians. No matter what ought to be the relations between such settlements and the aborigines,*

the fact is they do not get on together, and one or the other has to give way in the end. A system which looks to the extinction of a race is too abhorant for a Nation to indulge in without entailing upon the wrath of all Christendom, and without engendering in the Citizen a disregard for human life, and the rights of others, dangerous to society. I see no remedy for this except in placing all the indians on large reservations . . . and giving them absolute protection there.

The Indians were preparing for war and looked with contempt upon the white man's proposals. Finally the government decided to launch a military expedition into Indian territory under the command of General George Crook.

10.000 Indian braves
In May of 1876 a newly organized army decided to settle the Indian question once and for all. It formed into three columns. The first consisted of 1,200 soldiers commanded by Crook. It advanced from the north. The second, under the command of Colonel John Gibbon with 400 men, was positioned to the east. The third, commanded by General Alfred Terry, consisted of 1,300 soldiers and was assigned to attack from the south. Custer's Seventh Cavalry was part of this third column.

On the other side Sitting Bull had succeeded in assembling the greatest force of Native Americans ever brought together. His army was composed of 10,000 fighters (mainly Sioux and Cheyenne) and occupied an extensive area around the banks of the Little Bighorn River

Sitting Bull and Buffalo Bill Cody in 1885. Sitting Bull organized the Sioux and Cheyenne warriors that wiped out Custer's Seventh Cavalry.

(in present-day Montana). The message of this charismatic leader spread like wildfire, inspiring other prominent chiefs such as Chief Gall, as well as warriors such as Two Moons and Red Horse.

The Indians gained their first victory on June 17, 1876. Crazy Horse and his followers made a surprise attack on General Crook at the Battle of Rosebud, forcing the U.S. Army to retreat. The battle lasted seven hours. The Indians prevented reinforcements from coming from the north and Crook's company fell back to regroup.

For his part, General Terry, expecting the arrival of Gibbon's soldiers, ordered Custer and his cavalry to advance to the Little Bighorn River valley, where he believed Indian forces were gathered. He ordered Custer to wait until Terry's infantry arrived, at which point they could surround the Indians.

A poor decision

Custer was driven by ambition and saw this as a perfect opportunity to gain personal glory and recognition. He disobeyed orders and decided that he would attack the Indian camp. This questionable decision ended up costing many lives. At 2:30 in the afternoon of June 25 he divided his forces into three columns. Major Marcus Reno with 131 men was to follow Custer, and Captain Frederick Benteen, southwest of Custer, was to follow along the line of the hills just up to the Indian village.

Reno was the first to attack, but the Indians resisted, broke his line and forced him to retreat. This was when an impatient Custer decided to go on the attack. He led five companies (268 men) to the extreme north of the camp, planning to set upon the village from that direction. He was relying on support from Reno's men (who were by then beaten and scattered). Within a short time, Custer found himself completely surrounded by thousands of Indians. From that point everything happened very quickly. The nature of the terrain forced Custer's troops to dismount and fight hand to hand. Luck was not on their side. Gall's and Crazy Horse's braves attacked from every side, and in less than an hour all of the men of the Seventh Cavalry lay dead.

Three days later Terry's column came upon the scene. Most of the bodies had been despoiled of their guns and clothing. All the horses were gone. The body of Custer (who was called *Hi-Es-Tzie*, meaning "Long-hair") was discovered on a small hill, shot twice, once in the chest and once in the head.

The great gathering of Indian warriors quickly dispersed after the

battle. Sometime after the massacre Crazy Horse surrendered to the U.S. Army and, while under arrest, was killed under suspicious circumstances. Sitting Bull took refuge in Canada, only to return some years later and surrender to U.S. authorities.

This photograph from 1864 shows Custer in the uniform of the Union army with his wife Elizabeth Bacon Custer.

Over the years the Western Indians were persecuted and nearly annihilated by military actions and disease. It was not until 1924 that the U.S. government recognized the original Americans as citizens.

Botched Landing at Gallipoli

ERROR: A series of tactical mistakes obviated the effect of a surprise landing of soldiers and led to the British army being trapped for months by the Turks.

Who?
Future Prime Minister Winston Churchill (1874–1965), at that time First Lord of the Admiralty.

When?
April 25, 1915–January 9, 1916.

Consequences
The poorly executed disembarkation caused the deaths of 25,000 English, 10,000 French, 7,300 Australians, 2,400 New Zealanders and 1,700 Indians. The Turkish army suffered 100,000 deaths and 150,000 wounded.

There is no doubt that an amphibious landing on a hostile coastline is one of the trickiest of all military maneuvers. But the Allied landing at Gallipoli during the First World War was a debacle of epic proportions. The facts of the matter are as follows:

In February of 1915, what was called at the time "The Great War" had frozen into a stalemate. What initially looked to be a conflict of relatively short duration had turned into intractable combat. Trench warfare stymied all movement, leaving thousands of soldiers on both sides victims of hunger, disease and cold. The sides were evenly matched, which ruled out any easy solution. To the west were England and France, arrayed against the combined forces of Germany, the Austro-Hungarian Empire, Bulgaria and Turkey. On the eastern front Tsarist Russia harried a weakened Turkey without garnering much success. There was a clear need for decisive action to break the impasse.

Young Winston Churchill in a photograph from 1900, sixteen years before the disaster at Gallipoli. Although the full truth may never be known, historians tend to view the entire campaign as misguided.

Underestimating the Turks

Winston Churchill proposed an attack on Turkey with the goal of encircling the imperial troops. By seizing the Dardanelles Strait the Allies could join with Russian troops in the Black Sea and drive Turkey out of the war. The plan called for landing British troops on the Turkish peninsula of Gallipoli and proceeding from there to Istanbul, leaving behind the rearguard to deal with the Turks, thus circumventing Turkish defense of the strait. Everyone thought it was an excellent plan, except for a farseeing

British admiral, John Fisher, who tendered his resignation rather than lead his men on a mission that he was sure would end in failure. Sadly, he was absolutely right. However, nobody listened, and on April 25, 1915 a combined force of Australians and New Zealanders (the ANZACs) landed on the western part of the peninsula.

Whether because of darkness or simple incompetence, the beach on which the men landed, (later called Anzac Cove) turned out to be a narrow strip of land with a terrain that prevented the soldiers from pushing into the interior. Instead they had to seek refuge in caves and trenches and spent months repelling steady Turkish attacks. And where were the British and French troops? About 12 miles away in Helles, and in not much better shape than their Australian colleagues. Trapped between the sea and the surrounding high ground by Turkish forces under command of the German officer Otto Liman von Sanders, both wings of the Allied forces repeatedly attacked and were thrown back. As many as fifteen divisions had disembarked, and they were being depleted by withering Turkish fire. The element of surprise had been lost and rather than paving the way for a quick breakthrough, Allied forces were forced to withdraw to Egypt, after having been led to the slaughter on account of a

The Lancashire Rifles in May of 1915, en route to disaster. The element of surprise was lost when the Allied troops encountered much stiffer resistance than they had bargained for.

long series of tactical blunders on the part of their superior officers.

One reason for Turkey's success was the generalship of Mustafa Kemal (later to become Ataturk the first president of the Turkish republic). He command-

A **60-pound** British field artillery piece in action on Cape Helles.

ed the battle-hardened 19th Division, which had seen action the previous March and August, and they were able to successfully defend Turkish land against the invaders.

This bloody engagement inspired Peter Weir's film *Gallipoli*, which focused on the hardships endured and the extraordinary bonds formed by the Australian soldiers. It suggests that one reason for the defeat was that the landing site happened to be right where there was the greatest concentration of Turkish defenders.

The Gallipoli Syndrome

The resounding failure of the operation led to the resignation of its chief promoter, Winston Churchill. It also generated the so-called "Gallipoli syndrome," the future resistance to amphibious landings on enemy territory.

Fighting the Last War

ERROR: To rely upon the old Maginot Line, constructed along the Franco-German frontier during the First World War, to halt a German invasion.

When?
May 10–June 25, 1940.

Who?
Commander-in-Chief of the French Army, Maurice G. Gamelin (1872–1958).

Consequences
Victory of the German army and the ensuing capitulation of France.

I, for my part, acknowledge another precept which says that man must deal the final blow to those whose downfall is destined by God.

Adolf Hitler

After the end of the First World War the French were determined to prevent any more attacks from their bellicose German neighbors. So they took a leaf out of the ancient Romans' playbook (which proposed that Hadrian's Wall would be a sufficient defense against invading barbarians), and constructed a monumental line of defense along the frontier dividing the two countries. The plan was put into effect by André Maginot (whence the name), and a kind of Great Wall of China was built in France. It stretched for 250 miles, with 100 main fortifications spread out at a distance of 10 miles from one to the next, between which were smaller strongholds (called *petits ouvrages*). The defensive line looked to be impregnable. Except for a small detail. The line was constructed up to the Belgian border with only one gap: the wooded area of the Ardennes. The French commanders thought that it was impossible for an armed force of significant size to cross through the forest. Further, France and Belgium had reached a military accord in 1920 that permitted the French to move into Belgian territory if it was attacked by a third party. But the strategists did not plan for the unexpected.

Today visitors to the Maginot Line can see images such as this American tank. The German blitzkrieg simply went around the Line.

A futile line of defense

By the late 1930s Hitler had put the final touches on a terrifying military machine. He invaded Poland in September of 1939 and soon after that Norway and Denmark, without seeming to break a sweat. German troops were poised for action on the other side of the Maginot Line, and the Allies were becoming nervous. Whereas the aging

French Commander Maurice Gamelin adopted the defensive trench warfare strategy of World War I, the Germans brought new elements to the fight, such as armored vehicles and ground-and-air-coordinated strikes. Convinced that the Line could contain German troops coming from the east, the generals turned their attention to the Low Countries.

And here they met with their first unhappy surprise. Realizing that war with Germany would devastate their country, the Belgians quickly declared themselves neutral. Consequently, the French had to spread out their defenses along the Belgian frontier. But this line was much weaker than the heavily fortified Maginot Line, especially in comparison to the areas of Alsace and Lorraine. Acknowledging that he could no longer use Belgium as a battlefield, Gamelin moved the defensive line back to the French border to await the German forces moving through Belgium. He anticipated that this would be Germany's downfall. But he did not reckon with the acuity of the German commander Erich von Manstein. This brilliant strategist from Berlin used attacks on the northern flank in Belgium as a distraction, while secretly planning to cut through the "impenetrable" Ardennes Forest. Only two French divisions were positioned there. They were swatted away by Germany's 45 divisions of infantry and armored vehicles.

Getting closer

The German offensive began in the early morning of May 10, 1940. It took only two days for the Nineteenth Panzer Division under the command of Heinz Guderian to break through the Ardennes Forest. The French government had a panic attack, since up until this point they had completely dismissed the possibility of this threat. Fortunately, the Allies still had an ace up their sleeve. According to

U.S. troops crossing the Maginot Line in 1944. Behind them are cement pyramids built to impede tank movements.

the French generals the German tanks would not be able
to cross the Moselle River. Another miscalculation. At the
last moment the Luftwaffe launched a major bombardment
of French positions on the west side of the river. While the
French army was reeling from the effects of over 1,200
bombs, German engineers built a bridge in less than ten
hours. The British Royal Air Force sent 70 fighter planes
to destroy it, but they were met with a furious German an-
ti-aircraft barrage that prevented them from achieving
their objective. Only 31 British planes returned home.
Now the French position was becoming untenable. Each
day the Germans gained more ground, and Gamelin was
fired for incompetence. His replacement Marshal Weygand
put forth a plan. He ordered that the Anglo-French troops
that were trapped in the north and De Gaulle's tank divisions to the south launch simultaneous attacks on the ad-
vancing German troops. The plan ended in a genuine massacre for the Allies. It actually worsened the situation as
the Allies' weak showing convinced Mussolini to join the
party and declare war on France. In no time at all the country had lost its best defenses and best divisions.

81mm mortar from the
emplacements at Fort Saint
Gobain. It was never used.

Occupied France

On June 10 of 1940 the French government decamped
from Paris. Fifteen days later Hitler met with various
French high officials, who were seeking an armistice. The
accord stipulated that the Germans occupy two thirds of
France and called for the effective disbanding of the
French army. Although the French negotiators questioned
the severity of the conditions, the Germans refused to
yield an inch. Thus ended the Battle of France. France's
estimated losses were 100,000. Germany had lost just
7,000 men.

Back to Russia

ERROR: To invade the Soviet Union, underestimating the endurance of the Russian army and not taking "General Winter" into account.

Who?
Adolph Hitler, Chancellor of Germany.

When?
June–December 1941.

Consequences
Ignoring Napoleon's earlier adventure, Germany inflicted its most humiliating defeat on itself and had to abandon its project of total European domination.

The war against Russia will be such that it cannot be conducted in a knightly fashion. This struggle is one of ideologies and racial differences and will have to be conducted with unprecedented, unmerciful, and unrelenting harshness. All officers will have to rid themselves of obsolete ideologies. I know that the necessity for such means of waging war is beyond the comprehension of you generals but . . . I insist absolutely that my orders be executed without contradiction.

Adolf Hitler,

Hitler planned a rapid advance into Russia that would take him to Moscow before the weather turned. But delays plagued his army, and it found itself facing a particularly brutal winter.

By the middle of 1941 there seemed to be no end to Hitler's expansion in Europe. France and Holland had fallen along with Poland, Denmark, Luxembourg, Yugoslavia and Greece. Belgium had declared its neutrality. Italy had joined with the Third Reich and Romania, Bulgaria, Slovakia, Hungary and Finland all were satellites in the German orbit. The rest of the continent had declared neutrality or, as in Spain, claimed a non-combatant status.

After the German sweep through France, Hitler faltered in breaking English resistance. He decided to do to Russia what he had not succeeded in doing to Great Britain. In his imagination the Führer envisioned a German empire that would stretch from the Atlantic to the Ural Mountains. He had foreshadowed this in Mein Kampf:

> *And so we National Socialists consciously draw a line beneath the foreign policy tendency of our pre-War period. We take up where we broke off six hundred years ago. We stop the endless German movement to the south and west, and turn our gaze toward the land in the east. At long last we break off the colonial and commercial policy of the pre-War period and shift to the soil policy of the future.*

Hitler insisted on making all military decisions himself and proceeded into Russia over the objections of his generals.

Once conquered, the vast expanse of Russia would provide the German people with the *lebensraum* (living space) that it required and the resources to support a Reich that was to last for a thousand years. In addition, if Hitler had to face Great Britain in a long war of attrition he could bank on Russia to provide him with all the fuel and grain he would need.

Soon he found a name for his dream: Operation Barbarossa (in honor of Frederick Barbarossa, Holy Roman Emperor during what the Nazis referred to as the First Reich). The idea was to organize a blitzkrieg campaign that would annihilate the Russian army in single stroke. The plan was that the invasion would take only a few months and be finished before the onset of winter.

To avoid "General Winter," Hitler planned to launch the attack in May of 1941. According to his optimistic calculations the German army would be able to subdue the country in three months. In all, Hitler mobilized 3.2 million German soldiers, supplemented by another million men drawn from Germany's allies and occupied territories. Everything was ready for immediate action.

Then something happened that completely changed the situation. Mussolini found himself stymied by Allied troops in his attempted invasion of Greece. To throw his support behind the Italian dictator, Hitler had to open a road through Yugoslavia. After the devastating bombing of Belgrade, he was able to gain control of the country. A little while later Greece fell to the Germans, and Hitler could turn his attention back to the Eastern Front.

Hitler and Mussolini in June of 1940. Italy was the weak link in the Axis. The Allied invasion and Mussolini's fall allowed the Allies to encircle Germany.

He had secured his southern flank but in the process had lost precious time. A number of his generals stressed the risks that a mid-June attack could pose. The Führer ignored their advice and launched the offensive on June 22. At 3:15 in the morning four million soldiers advanced along a gigantic front stretching 1,000 miles from the Baltic to the Black Sea. The German forces were organized into 225 divisions and furnished with 7,000 artillery pieces, 4,400 tanks and 4,000 planes. This constituted the largest military force ever assembled.

For the first few weeks everything went according to plan. The German general Franz Halder boasted: "One can already say that the task of destroying the mass of the Red Army has been fulfilled. It is no exaggeration to claim that the campaign against Russia was won in 14 days."

German soldiers in a trench huddle together against the cold.

Field Marshal Feodor von Bock was in charge of Operation Barbarossa. He died in a bombing raid in the spring of 1945.

Operation Typhoon

It looked like Russia would fall within a few days, when the weather intervened for the Soviets. Torrential rains arrived, making roads impassable in the middle of July. The northern and southern army groups delayed their advance, and Hitler made an unfortunate decision. He halted the central group's advance on Moscow in favor of supporting the other two groups. The advance on Moscow, named Operation Typhoon, was delayed until October 2. Hitler planned to blow up the entire city and wipe it off the map. He then intended to build a huge dam that would supply hydro-electric power and submerge Moscow under water.

But rain and snow continued to fall, and when German troops were about 50 miles from the city, flooded roads bogged down the heavily armed infantry. The majority of tanks, trucks, motorcycles and armored vehicles were stuck in the mud. The rain continued and with it falling temperatures. By November temperatures were going down to minus 10 degrees centigrade, taking many armored vehicles and tanks out of commission. It turned out that there were insufficient supplies of anti-freeze. The German soldiers under the command of Feodor von Bock were unprepared for this kind of situation. Their clothing was clearly inadequate, as were supply lines that had not been designed to support such an immense number of troops for so long a period of time.

By the end of November, the conditions for the German army had become truly dire. The thermometer dipped to historic lows, as cold as minus 45 degrees. The number of deaths from exposure far exceeded those brought on by enemy action. German generals wanted to dig in and wait until spring to renew the offensive. Meanwhile Stalin had ordered scorched-earth tactics. Pasture land, farms, livestock, everything was to be completely destroyed, thereby denying provisions to the Germans.

Hitler ordered his troops to advance to Moscow and launch a final attack on the capital. In the city, the Soviets had mustered a defensive army of 1.2 million soldiers, supplied with 8,000 cannons and mortars, and about a thousand tanks. All the city's occupants had been mobilized to dig trenches, raise barricades and gunners' nests to deny entry to the invaders.

Hitler planned to enter the Kremlin a few hours after the final offensive, but the Soviets managed to deny him bragging rights. Stalin had ordered troops stationed in Siberia to be redeployed relying on a non-aggression treaty with Japan and on information transmitted by a Soviet spy in Tokyo, Richard Sorge. Logistical problems combined with staunch Russian resistance finally doomed Barbarossa, forcing the humiliating retreat of the Nazi army.

Russian soldiers in 1941 preparing to face the enemy. The Red Army followed the same strategy that their great grandfathers had used against Napoleon: retreat and draw the Germans deep into the country, and then attack the retreating invaders.

Could the "Day of Infamy" Have Been Avoided?

ERROR: To react too slowly to news of an imminent Japanese attack on the naval base at Pearl Harbor.

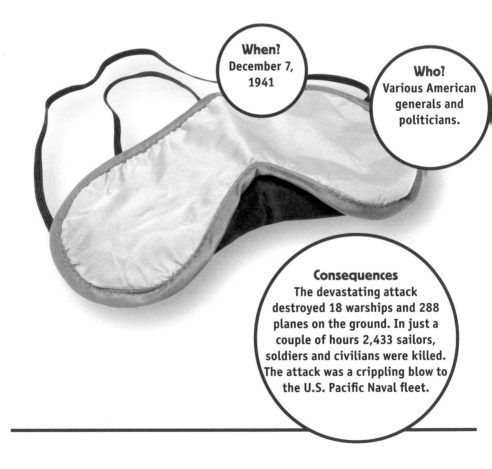

When?
December 7, 1941

Who?
Various American generals and politicians.

Consequences
The devastating attack destroyed 18 warships and 288 planes on the ground. In just a couple of hours 2,433 sailors, soldiers and civilians were killed. The attack was a crippling blow to the U.S. Pacific Naval fleet.

Yesterday, Dec. 7, 1941 — a date which will live in infamy — the United States of America was suddenly and deliberately attacked by naval and air forces of the Empire of Japan.

President Roosevelt's address to Congress.

Americans have three dates engraved in their collective memory: September 11, the day of the bombing of the World Trade Center; November 23, the date of John F. Kennedy's assassination; and December 7, the bombing of Pearl Harbor. It is the last of these that we will be looking at here.

Most if not all wars are due to conflicting economic interests. To understand why Japan decided to enter into the Second World War,

The U.S.S. *California* was sunk in the bombing raid on Pearl Harbor.

one needs to consider its problematic relationship with China, its neighbor and rival. In 1937 the two countries butted heads in the Sino-Japanese War. Japan's expansionism overstepped certain limits and with the fall of France in 1940, it occupied some European colonies, such as French Indochina. In response, the U.S. and Great Britain implemented a blockade. Japan's economy depended upon imported metals and petroleum, which was especially important since Japan had no domestic petroleum supplies, so the imposition of the embargo occasioned severe economic distress. Supplies of other necessary raw materials such as rubber, coal and

Secretary of State Cordell Hull was responsible for the letter (named the Hull Note) that demanded the Japanese relinquish their gains in China and Southeast Asia. Hull received the Noble Peace Prize in 1945 for his role in the creation of the United Nations.

copper were halted as well. As this tactic was beginning to exercise a stranglehold on Japan's economy, negotiations were undertaken to arrive at some compromise. The U.S. government dispatched the Hull Note, (formally titled "Outline of Proposed Basis for Agreement Between the United States and Japan") that insisted that Japan withdraw from China and French colonies. The Japanese responded angrily, labeling it as blackmail and provocation. On the same day they began preparing for the attack on Pearl Harbor.

Operation Z

Japan saw no other alternative to launching the attack. As Hideki Tojo, Japan's Commander-in-Chief and Prime Minister, was said to have remarked: "To do nothing is to ensure the destruction of Japan." The surprise attack on Port Arthur that started the Sino-Russian War in 1904 served as inspiration for Isoroku Yamamoto, Japanese Naval Commander. He suggested that a single devastating attack on American naval bases in Hawaii was the best way to destroy America's threatening Pacific fleet. And while the U.S. was engaged in rebuilding, the Japanese could take over American and European possessions in Asia and Oceania.

The U.S. base of operations in the Hawaiian archipelago was situated at Pearl Harbor. Located on the island of Oahu, it was about ten miles from Hawaii's capital, Honolulu. It was a key jumping-off place for U.S. operations in the Pacific.

Once decided upon, the attack was named Operation Z, in honor of the Z flag that initiated the Japanese attack in the Battle of Tsushima, the decisive naval engagement in the Sino-Russian War that destroyed the Russian fleet and caused the deaths of 4,380 men.

Yamamoto fixed the date for the attack for the morning of December 7.

A slow response

The tactical decision was to declare war on the U.S. shortly before the commencement of the attack. The Japanese Foreign Minister's office relayed a coded message to its ambassador in Washington. The announcement was received by the U.S. authorities while Japanese planes were underway to their target. But the message was secretly intercepted and decoded by the Center for Naval Intelligence in Maryland. Its contents were sent to Admiral Harold Stark, Chief of Naval Operations. One of his officers realized that the projected time for breaking off negotiations coincided with dawn in Honolulu and the perfect time for an attack. He conveyed his suspicions to Army Chief of Staff George C. Marshall. At that time Marshall was horseback riding and did not return to his office until some hours later. When he finally read the Japanese declaration, he sent a radio alert. But atmospheric conditions in the Pacific prevented it from getting through. So he had to resort to a commercial cable, which had the effect of diminishing the urgency of the message. The alert reached Hawaii just a few minutes before the start of the attack.

Isoroku Yamamoto was the most capable Japanese admiral and commander-in-chief of the Japanese Combined Fleet. He studied at Harvard and was well acquainted with his enemies. He died when the plane he was traveling in was shot down in the spring of 1943.

The USS *Shaw* going up in flames during the Japanese attack.

A devastating bombardment.

The Japanese naval and air armada that prepared for the attack was impressive. It consisted of six aircraft carriers, two battleships, two heavy cruisers, one light cruiser, 8 destroyers, 81 fighters, 135 dive bombers, 104 horizontal bombers, 40 torpedo bombers and 3 fuel tankers. The attack on the American base was conducted in two waves; the first came at 7: 53 A.M. on Sunday, December 7, 1941. It was headed by torpedo bombers, which focused their energies on American aircraft carriers and battleships. Meanwhile, other bombers attacked the Air Force bases at Hickam and

Wheeler Air Fields.

The planes of the second wave attacked Bellows Field, a naval air base, and Ford Island, in the center of Pearl Harbor. The surprise attack was devastating. Ninety minutes after it began, it was over. In total, the Japanese sank 18 ships: 188 U.S. aircraft were destroyed on the ground. 2,433 sailors, soldiers and civilians were killed. Almost half (1,102 men) died in the explosion and sinking of the battleship USS Arizona. The 35-ton-ship crumpled like a sheet of paper when a projectile fell from a high altitude bomber, penetrated the ship's outer armor and detonated in the forward compartment where weapons were stored.

Mitsubishi A6M Zero. This was the kind of long-range plane that flew on the bombing mission at Pearl Harbor.

Did FDR let it happen?

Many people continue to accuse the American government of having done nothing to prevent the attack on Pearl Harbor. Among other data, their claims find support in the diary of Secretary of War Henry Stimson: "FDR brought up the event that we were likely to be attacked perhaps next Monday [December 1], for the Japanese are notorious for making an attack without warning, and the question was what we should do. The question was how we should maneuver them into the position of firing the first shot without allowing too much danger to ourselves."

Revisionist historians note that Roosevelt had wanted to enter the war as early as 1940, further pointing to more than 100 messages saved in the National Archives intercepted from Japanese planes during their journey across the Pacific to Pearl Harbor. Despite all this, the naval base received no advance warning. The question why is still an open one.

BUSINESS!

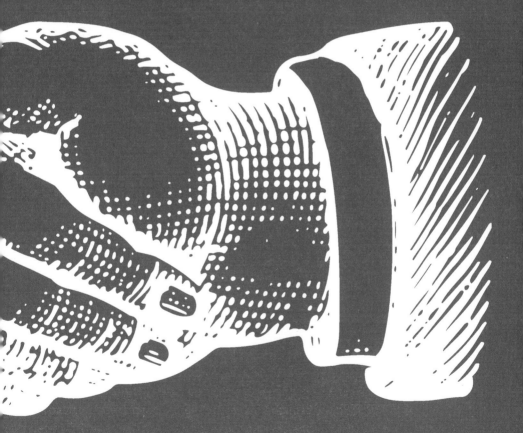

Black Thursday

ERROR: The acute imbalance between supply and demand, excessive speculation, buying stocks on margin, and the lack of regulation and oversight on the part of the U.S. government brought on a worldwide economic depression that lasted for many years.

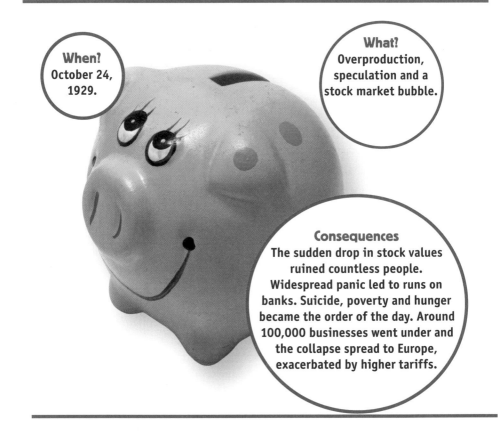

When?
October 24, 1929.

What?
Overproduction, speculation and a stock market bubble.

Consequences
The sudden drop in stock values ruined countless people. Widespread panic led to runs on banks. Suicide, poverty and hunger became the order of the day. Around 100,000 businesses went under and the collapse spread to Europe, exacerbated by higher tariffs.

*With impressive proof on all sides of magnificent prog-
ress, no one can rightly deny the fundamental correct-
ness of our economic system.*
President Herbert Hoover

The decade of the 1920s was an
exuberant time in America. It was
a period of general prosperity and
intense industrial productivity
brought about by a profound
transformation in technology and
manufacturing processes. There
were no real drags on growth, and
consumption increased. The mass-
es began to buy cars and electric
appliances that had formerly been
available only to the wealthiest
segments of society. The middle
class was flourishing and filled
with a sense of optimism. The
president, Herbert Hoover,
summed up the general euphoria.

The American economy grew
very quickly and became
overly reliant upon its
financial sector. Millions of
people invested in the stock
market and saw their savings
wiped out. The photo shows
an expensive car offered for
sale at a fraction of its price.

*Unemployment in the sense of distress is widely disap-
pearing. . . . We in America today are nearer to the final
triumph over poverty than ever before in the history of
any land. The poor-house is vanishing from among us.
We have not yet reached the goal, but given a chance to
go forward with the policies of the last eight years, we
shall soon with the help of God be in sight of the day
when poverty will be banished from this nation.*

And at the time all of this was true. The booming automobile, steel and construction industries generated

plenty of good jobs. The U.S. unemployment rate had never been lower. Technological advances reduced manufacturing costs, and increased the general welfare. Truly morning in America! And Wall Street was leading the way. Share prices were climbing to astronomical levels. The economic bonanza had converted thousands of Americans to the gospel of easy money, as stock values kept rising.

Black Thursday

By early in 1929 stockbrokers had been loaning huge amounts of money to small investors without any guarantees other than rising share values. This served to inflate the bubble further. But salaries could not keep up and little by little demand began to fall off. Factories began to fill up with unsold goods, and companies began to lay off workers.

And yet confidence continued unabated. The euphoria shattered into a thousand pieces on Thursday, October 24, 1929, known as Black Thursday. The value of the New York Stock Exchange collapsed. As many as 13 million shares offered for sale could not find buyers, causing the Exchange to capsize. This massive sell-off brought the vibrant progess of the 1920s to a screeching halt.

Over the following days the crisis deepened. There did not seem to be any way to stop the fall. For a while the government remained convinced that this was just a passing phase, a correction, and things would soon return to normal. So nothing was done to address the basic economic imbalances or slow the accelerating rate of unemployment until it was too late. And so the crisis worsened. The high level of public debt was unsustainable, and banks became insolvent. The Crash of 1929 signaled a worldwide period of economic contraction that is known as the Great Depression. America's troubles

The New York Stock Exchange is an international institution. It was created in 1817 by a group of stockbrokers to buy and sell shares.

spilled over its borders, dragging down European markets and hitting especially hard those nations most dependent upon trade with U.S.

The New Deal

In the next decade those nations most affected by the Depression tried different approaches to correct the worsening economic conditions. This era witnessed the birth of Keynesian economics, named after the celebrated British economist John Maynard Keynes (1883–1946). He concluded that the crisis was caused by insufficient demand and that government intervention was needed to stimulate the economy. The rebalancing of supply and demand ought to result in an increase in demand, which would offset excessive supply. To accomplish this the state should resort to deficit spending. This entailed investment in public works projects and boosting those sectors of the economy that would have the most impact on employment. The idea was to enhance the buying power of the widest swath of the population while protecting the income of the poorest members of society. These revolutionary ideas were put into practice by the newly elected U.S. president, Franklin Delano Roosevelt (1882–1945). Known as the New Deal, Roosevelt's politics inaugurated a new era of liberalism, establishing an economic policy in which the government would take an active role.

People on a bread line ironically posed against the backdrop of a poster touting the American way of life.

One of the most haunting images from the Great Depression, this photograph entitled *Migrant Mother*, was taken by Dorothea Lange in 1936.

The Beatles?
Never Heard of Them

ERROR: To pass up the opportunity to sign the most successful musical group of all time.

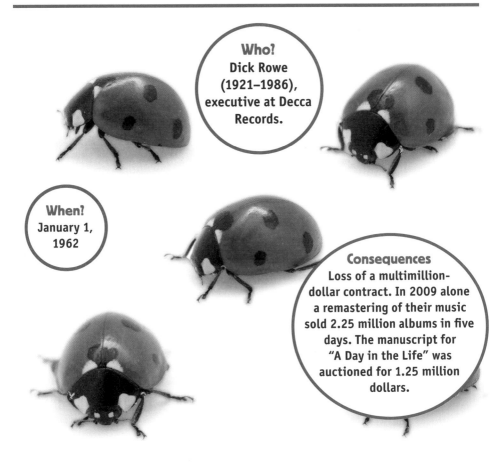

Who?
Dick Rowe
(1921–1986),
executive at Decca
Records.

When?
January 1,
1962

Consequences
Loss of a multimillion-dollar contract. In 2009 alone a remastering of their music sold 2.25 million albums in five days. The manuscript for "A Day in the Life" was auctioned for 1.25 million dollars.

He's a real nowhere man.

Lennon & McCartney

On July 6, 1957 Paul McCartney went with his friend Ivan Vaughn to hear a Liverpool band in concert. It was called The Quarrymen and was founded by four school friends, from the Quarry Bank School, one of whom was John Lennon. Vaughn and Lennon were friends, and at the end of the concert Lennon stopped by to talk for a while. Paul, who played the guitar, was looking to join a band and asked if there was room for him in the group. After doing a cover of Eddie Cochran's classic "Twenty Flight Rock," Paul was invited to join the band. A little while later Lennon and McCartney united with George Harrison, another guitarist, and Stuart Sutcliffe on bass. Drummers came and went.

The Beatles are still the most successful rock group of all time. They auditioned for Dick Rowe for over an hour but he declined to sign them up. He later made up somewhat for his mistake by signing the Rolling Stones.

The band went through a few names (Johnny and the Moondogs, The Silver Beetles) when Sutcliffe came up with the name Beatals, in homage of Buddy Holly and his group the Crickets. Finally, the boys decided on The Beatles and the band was launched, although still without a drummer. They ended up hiring Pete Best for the vacant position and started on their career. After an

Brian Epstein became the Beatles' manager in December of 1961. He played a leading role in the band's early success.

extended stay in Hamburg, Germany, the band returned to Liverpool, where they developed a following at the now legendary Cavern Club, located at 10 Mathew Street. Between 1961 and 1963 the group gave almost 300 performances there. In 1962 Ringo Starr replaced Best on drums.

The band was finally discovered by Brian Epstein. Some years later he would recall their first meeting:

> *I was immediately struck by their music, their beat and their sense of humor on stage. And, even afterwards, when I met them, I was struck again by their personal charm. And it was there that, really, it all started.*

A no from Decca

Epstein was a smart businessman and became the driving force behind the initial promotion and success of the group. But breaking into a new business is never easy. The large companies he approached turned their backs on him and signed other bands. This was the case with Decca in one the most often mentioned episodes in the history of the music industry. The famous "Decca audition" took place on January 1, 1962, right before the group was heading off on a world tour. It took place in Decca's recording studio in West Hampstead, in North London. The band played 15 songs in a little less than an hour. Everything went well, and the Decca executives present decided to record some of their music. A few weeks later Dick Rowe, head of Decca's music division, let the Beatles' manager know that he was going to pass. According to George Harrison, Rowe told Brian Epstein, "Guitar groups are on their way out, Mr. Epstein."

Decca's name comes from a portable gramophone called a Decca Dulcephone, patented in 1914. In this case the company seriously dropped the ball but in the next

In 1939 Decca was the only record company in the U.K. It achieved its greatest success in the 1960s but began to lose ground in 1970 when the Rolling Stones signed with another label.

one hit it out of the park. Shortly after turning his back on the Beatles, Rowe signed a contract with some other young Brits, their Satanic Majesties, the Rolling Stones, who still rival the Beatles' claim to being the best band in rock & roll history. Interestingly, it was George Harrison, who suggested that Rowe listen to the Stones.

After being rejected by Decca, the Beatles were turned down by Columbia, Pye, Philips and Oriole. Finally, in 1962, Epstein landed a contract with EMI, one of the most successful operations in the business. Signed by John, Paul, George and Ringo, along with Paul's and George's parents (since they were under 21), the contract paved the way for the Beatles' first hit, "Love Me Do," which reached number 17 on the UK charts. The rest is history.

In the beginning, the Beatles were rejected by all the major U.K. record companies.

Olympic Debacle in Montreal

ERROR: To hold the Olympic games without adequate funding.

When?
July 17–August 1, 1976.

Who?
Jean Drapeau, Mayor of Montreal, in charge of preparations for the 1976 Summer Olympics.

Consequences
His gross underestimation of the costs associated with holding the Games led to an immense public debt. The final tally reached 1.2 billion Canadian dollars. The Canadian public had to pay specially imposed taxes to cover the shortfall for a number of years.

The Olympics logo of five interlocked rings was created in 1913 and brought to public attention by Pierre de Coubertin, founder of the International Olympic Committee.

The history of the Olympic games is filled with notable successes and failures. One of the worst in the second category occurred in 1976. The Montreal Games got off on the wrong foot from the very beginning. The preceding Olympics, held in Munich in 1972, were the site of an attack by Palestinian commandos on the Israeli compound in the Olympic Village. The Palestinian group, called Black September, killed eleven Israeli athletes. International reaction was intense, leading to security precautions never seen before. At no time were there fewer than 15,000 security officers on duty to watch over the Games in Montreal.

Jean Drapeau was the Mayor of Montreal from 1954 to 1957 and again from 1960 to 1986. To finance the Olympic Games, he instituted the first state-run lottery in Canada.

There were also political controversies. African countries boycotted the Games that year because of New Zealand's presence. This was the period of apartheid in South Africa, and the New Zealand rugby team had gone on a tour of the country. This led to the boycott. And things didn't stop here. The IOC refused to allow Taiwan to participate, thus denying its national identity.

Montreal's Olympic Village was designed by the architect René Lépine.

Montreal's Olympic Stadium cost a considerable amount to maintain. It featured a retractable roof.

An onerous debt

The political and security problems added pressure to the teetering financial structure that was supposed to support the Games. Montreal would turn out to be most ruinous episode in Olympic history. From the very beginning the Canadian government displayed extreme reluctance to underwrite any of the costs. So it was left to local authorities and the city of Montreal to assume

the major part of the responsibilities. Neither the national government in Ottawa nor the provincial government in Quebec lent the city a hand. Montreal's mayor, Jean Drapeau (1916–1999) tried to come up with ways to raise money. He created an Olympic lottery, confirmed million-dollar contracts with television stations and sold commercial rights to the use of the Olympic mascot, Amik. By such moves, the local authorities tried to show that the Games could finance themselves.

In the end the city was able to raise 300 million dollars, which allowed work to get started. That only got them in deeper. The costs for renovation and construction of the city's infrastructure, the Olympic Village, the stadium and other installations came to a total of over 1.2 billion dollars. The result: years of tax increases, heavy debt and increasing social tensions.

Seville Expo

Another major municipal blunder was the International Expo in Seville in 1992. Before the Expo was scheduled to be held, anyone visiting the site would have found empty lots, abandoned docked ships in dry dock and some minimal industrial activity. The initial estimate of 275 million euros skyrocketed to 1.4 billion. Most of the construction work was awarded without competitive bidding and later investigation revealed numerous financial irregularities. The one bright spot was that some of the new construction could be repurposed. But that slight benefit in no way compensated for the squandering of such an immense outlay of capital.

E.T. Doesn't Like M&Ms

ERROR: To refuse the chance of having M&Ms play a leading role in Steven Spielberg's E.T., one of the highest grossing pictures of all time.

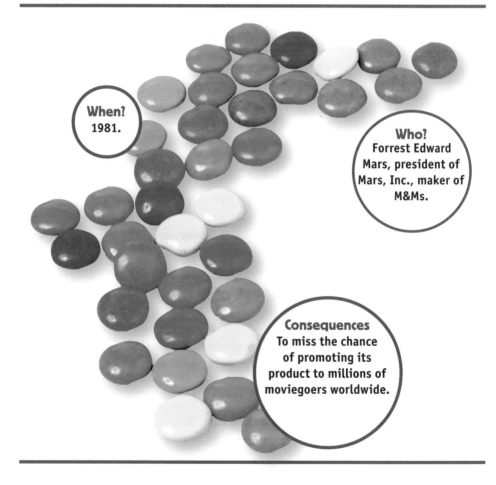

When?
1981.

Who?
Forrest Edward Mars, president of Mars, Inc., maker of M&Ms.

Consequences
To miss the chance of promoting its product to millions of moviegoers worldwide.

Surely you remember this scene:

There is no way that E.T. is going to come out of hiding. To overcome his fear, the young protagonist, Elliot, places a row of chocolates on the floor as bait. The trick gives birth to one of the most exploited marketing strategies ever since: what is now referred to as "product placement."

Until the release of this film, brands and products shown in movies appeared just to promote realism and enhance the atmosphere of the story. They were not seen as advertisements and did not contribute financially to the production. That is until 1982 when Steven Spielberg picked up the phone and called the Mars company. The idea was to use its popular candy M&M's in the scene in exchange for the company's financing part of the movie. The response of the president, Forrest Edward Mars, son of the company's founder, was clear: There was no way that he would allow Spielberg to mention his flagship brand in connection with an ugly alien who would most certainly scare his young customers away. Thus, "the chocolate that melts in your mouth, not in your hand" starred in one of the most notorious bungles in business history.

The opportunity that Mars rejected was accepted by the Hershey Foods Company for its Reese's Pieces. The two candies are somewhat similar, although Reese Peanut Butter cups have a soft chocolate shell with a peanut butter filling, instead of chocolate; they also have a circular shape but aren't coated with different flavored candy colors. Shortly after its release on June 11, 1982, sales of Reese's Pieces, the Oscar-winning E.T.'s favorite candy, increased by 65 percent. Out of this world delicious!

ET's telephone, built by his human friend Elliott with the hope of contacting the spaceship that had abandoned him on Earth.

It Seemed Like a Good Idea

ERROR: Changing the taste of Coca-Cola to create a new product that would better compete with Pepsi.

Who?
Roberto C. Goizueta, CEO of the Coca-Cola Company.

When?
April 23, 1985.

Consequences
The new flavor was a total disaster. The public gave it an enthusiastic thumbs down. The company received 400,000 letters and cards protesting the decision, the protestors even going so far as to form an organization in honor of the original flavor. Finally, the company had to backpedal and resume production of the old flavor. Strangely enough, Coke not only recovered the ground it lost in the fiasco but got a bump in sales.

"Have you tried it?"

"Yes."

"Did you like it?"

"Yes, but I'll be damned if I'll let Coca-Cola know that."

Conversation overheard by Coca-Cola executive

regarding New Coke

The first canned sodas appeared on the market in 1953. But it was not until 1959 that they were sold internationally.

It was 1984, Coca-Cola's centenary year, but not all was gladness and light. The company was going through an unprecedented crisis and losing ground to its main competitor, Pepsi. Until that point, the company had had little to worry about. Sales of Coke led Pepsi by a margin of two to one. But two brilliant advertising campaigns had turned the tables. The first, "Join the Pepsi Generation," convinced the public that Pepsi was the drink for young people, not Coca-Cola, which was for their parents' generation. The campaign targeted the key demographic: young people wanting to change and try new things. Pepsi 1, Coke 0. The following season ad men presented "The Pepsi Challenge." Viewers saw blindfold tests that showed that people trying Coke and Pepsi, not knowing which was which, chose Pepsi. 2–0.

The worst decision in the history of marketing

As simply as that, things started to

Coca-Cola logo with its classic glass bottle. Coke tried many different sizes and formats to attract customers. But its distinctive bottle modeled after a woman's body is recognizable the world over.

change. Month by month Pepsi began to close the gap with its rival. The directors of Coca-Cola did not sit on their hands. They concluded that even though Coca-Cola had more outlets, more extensive distribution and exclusives with chains like McDonald's, Pepsi was nipping at its heels, it must be because Coke tasted worse. So Roberto Goizueta, in a real act of bravado, made the worst decision known in the history of marketing: change the taste of Coca-Cola. Until that moment no one had dared touch the sacrosanct formula of the world's most famous drink. But after months of hard work and many tests, he launched New Coke, with a sweeter and smoother taste than its predecessor. Coke withdrew the old flavor from supermarkets and supported the launch with a mega advertising campaign.

It was the biggest failure in the history of business. People rejected the new flavor, felt deceived by the company and protested the change to one of the country's most recognizable icons. The company was inundated with angry letters and cards.

Sales plummeted. Finally, the company reversed itself, downplaying the new flavor (now known as New Coke) in favor of the original recipe, which was now known as Coca-Cola Classic. Curiously, the brand not only recovered the ground it had lost in three short months, it obtained the much desired market share advantage over Pepsi. That year, Coca-Cola achieved record sales, which led to a multimillion-dollar bonus for Chairman Roberto Goizueta, despite being the mastermind behind the launch of New Coke. Some cynics speculated that the whole thing had been planned, to which a Coca-Cola executive responded, "We're not that smart."

Ad campaigns gone wrong

Multinationals should be careful when they enter a new market with translations of the names of their products and, above all, with the translations of their advertising campaigns, because they can easily be misinterpreted. This has led to costly mistakes.

Sometimes the error is prevented in time. For example, for the Spanish market Mitsubishi was able to change the name of its all-terrain model Pajero, which is slang for someone who masturbates constantly, to Montero, and Ford was able to change the name of its Pinto model in Brazil, slang for "small testicles," to the Corcel. The Swedish Electrolux appliance factory entered the United States announcing their vacuum cleaners with the slogan: "Nothing sucks like an Electrolux." Not exactly the image the company was trying to cultivate.

Another type of error was made by Pepsi in India when a child serving Pepsi appeared in one of its ads, neglecting to take note of the controversies over child labor laws in that country. Perhaps the worst ad campaign in recent memory was for Malaysia Airlines, which launched "My Ultimate Bucket List Contest" for customers in Australia and New Zealand in 2014 after suffering two tragic downed flights in the same year.

Subprime Meltdown

ERROR: The attitude that good times would last forever led to gross miscalculations of the risks resulting from the sale of toxic financial instruments (subprime mortgages).

When?
2007.

Who?
The financial and real estate sectors of the U.S. economy.

Consequences
A profound liquidity crisis leading to business failures, bankruptcies, high unemployment and global recession.

It all began with historically low rates in the early 2000s. This encouraged a speculative bubble especially in connection with real estate, since it freed up an immense amount of capital. Homes were selling like hot cakes, and this continued through 2004. At that point interest rates started inching up. After the party comes the hangover. Serious problems cropped up with many properties. By the beginning of 2007 the situation had become critical and started to result in a large number of foreclosures as a result of mortgages lent at subprime rates. These mortgages were intended to draw people from lower economic levels into the housing market. However, many of the loans had adjustable rates of interest and had been sold in a predatory fashion (convincing people to take out mortgages that they clearly could not af-

The Eccles Building in Washington D.C., home of the Federal Reserve.

The International Monetary Fund (IMF) has been accused of administering shock therapy to countries in crisis and adding to their economic woes by demanding austerity.

ford). In 2006 the total value of subprime mortgages rose to 20 percent of all mortgage lending from an average of 8 percent a few years earlier. Housing prices began to decline from their peak. In February HSBC, became the first major institution to have to write down mortgage holdings.

Debt kept mounting, affecting the entire financial system. But the debt was repackaged and sold from one institution to another using complex devices such CDOs (collateralized debt obligations) and various kinds of mortgage-backed securities (MBS). This postponed the day of reckoning, allowing people to ignore the problem or pretend that it didn't exist.

The first domino falls

Many of the subprime mortgages had been made at adjustable rates. As interest rates rose, mortgage payments increased dramatically, and many poorer borrowers were unable to keep up. Housing prices were declining, and they could not refinance. For a while, despite the increasing number of foreclosures, it seemed like things could be kept under control. Then, in March of 2007, the second largest mortgage company in the country, New Century Financial, got into difficulties and suspended lending. It declared bankruptcy in April. It was not the only company to do so. A short while after, Accredited Home Lenders Holding, a company specializing in high-risk mortgages, went belly up. Losses from subprime lending were mounting.

Crisis in the financial system

The downward trend picked up speed in August. On August 2 the investment group Blackstone declared bankruptcy. Two days later American Home Mortgage (the tenth largest mortgage bank in the U.S.) laid off all of its staff and declared bankruptcy on August 6. By now the crisis had crossed the Atlantic. On August 9 the French Bank BNP Paribas announced that it was halting redemptions on three of its funds due to subprime problems.

Now things were spiraling downwards. Loss of confidence led to near panic, which swept through the global financial system. Markets turned bearish, share values were hit hard, and a liquidity crunch ensued.

Things went from bad to worse. The Federal Reserve and the European Central Bank were forced to inject unheard of amounts of cash into the banking system. The ECB put almost one trillion euros into circulation to calm nervous markets, while the Fed pumped 240 billion dollars into the U.S. economy. But the crisis continued to spread. In Europe major banks started to admit that they were in serious trouble. As the collapse gathered momentum it appeared that they could not avoid bankruptcy. Major mortgage lending institutions fell one after another.

The European Central Bank laid out billions of euros to prop up the banking system in Europe during the depth of the financial crisis brought on by sub-prime mortgages.

The fall of Lehman Brothers

2008 was not better. The crisis that had so far been limited to the financial sector began to infect the rest of the economy, partly as a result of the high levels of public debt. In April the IMF figured that 945 billion dollars had been lost during the crisis. July witnessed the rescue of Freddie Mac and Fannie Mae by the Federal government at a cost of an additional 200 billion dollars. In September, Lehman Brothers, the fourth largest investment bank in the U.S., declared bankruptcy. Lehman Brothers had been founded in 1850 and was in many ways a symbol of the stability of the American financial system.

Upon arriving in the White House, President Barack Obama was confronted with the possibility of a global economic depression. His decision to inject vast amounts of money into the banking system contrasted with the more cautious approach taken in Europe.

No easy fix

The crisis had now been going on for over a year and there was no end in sight. In November a new president was elected, the Democrat, Barack Obama. By this time Wall Street had given up over 10 percent of its value. In February 2009 the World Bank announced that 100 million people had fallen below the poverty line on account of the economic crisis. The U.S. government decided to inject more money into the economy. This increased public and private debt, but was a necessary step to forestall what seemed likely to become a global depression. Looking back now, it seems clear that the so-called economic experts had no idea what was going on, govern-

ment bodies in charge of financial oversight were missing in action, and both financial institutions and the general public had been engaged in a reckless spending spree. All of this contributed to a situation that threatened the closely integrated global economy. It was a close call. As one observer noted: "The whole house of cards was about to come tumbling down."

At the height of the crisis foreclosures reached a record level with many homeowners underwater (owing more than their homes were worth).

TECHNOLOGY

What Could Go Wrong?

ERROR: Costly mistakes

When?
Every epoch since the beginning of the Industrial Revolution.

Who?
Engineers, geologists, architects, economists and politicians, in short, anyone whose decisions could go wrong.

Consequences
Loss of life, harm to the environment, food supplies and infrastructure and the multitude of problems that come about when one does not sufficiently take into account the laws of nature.

Engineering can be defined as the application of technical and scientific knowledge to resolve problems that directly affect humanity. The work of engineers has made all of our lives easier...sometimes. There have been other instances where the engineering fixes have not worked out that well.

At left is a fragment of the Saint Francis Dam that collapsed in 1928. The dam was poorly constructed on an unstable foundation.

- When you are going to build a dam that is to hold back millions of gallons of water, it is advisable to investigate the geological conditions of the area before work begins. On March 12, 1928 the Saint Francis Dam (about 40 miles from Los Angeles) collapsed because of a tectonic fault that the engineer William Mulholland had simply overlooked. 450 people died as a result. Following the accident, the panel in charge of analyzing the responsibilities arising from the dam failure found that it was caused by errors in engineering and inadequate geologic studies. Their report concluded that a project of this magnitude should never be left to one person alone, no matter how qualified.

- On July 17, 1981 celebrations were halted during a crowded dance contest at the Kansas City Hyatt Regency Hotel when suspended platforms in the interior of the building collapsed killing 114 people. The error? The structures were insufficiently reinforced due to cost and scheduling pressures.

- Do you know which ship sank in the shortest period of time? The answer is the *Vasa*, a Swedish warship built in the seventeenth century by orders of King Gustavus Adolphus. She was launched from Stockholm on August 10, 1628. Just after leaving the dock on her maiden voyage, the ship was struck by a strong gust of wind. The *Vasa* keeled over and the water began to enter the cannon ports. In addition, the boat's design was too high relative to its beam. Finally, the accumulation of water in the hold precipitated its collapse.

Portrait of Gustavus Adolphus, King of Sweden by Matthaus Merian. The king commissioned the construction of the warship Vasa that sank on its maiden voyage.

- The dirigible industry has been responsible for some terrible disasters. Two tragic accidents within seven years of each other, ended the dirigible's prospects of becoming a commercially viable alternative to plane travel. The first accident occurred on the *R-101*, a British model that crashed killing 48 of its 54 passengers. The second dramatic accident was to the *Hindenburg*. 36 people died when it caught fire landing in New Jersey.

- The Citicorp Center is one of the tallest skyscrapers in New York, easily recognizable by its truncated roof. It is located on Lexington Avenue and 53rd Street. But before construction began the architects had to agree to conditions set by one of the

lot's occupants, St. Peter's Lutheran Church. The Church had decided to erect a new building for itself and insisted that it be entirely distinct from the Citicorp Center. That is, the building would have to go up around it.This requirement created numerous difficulties but finally the structural engineer, William LeMessurier, came up with a workaround. His idea was to support the edifice with

The age of the dirigible ended with the *Hindenburg* disaster.

The Citicorp building stands out among New York's skyscrapers for its distinctive slanted roof. It had to be built around an old Lutheran church jeopardizing the entire construction.

four enormous columns, one hundred feet high each, and locate them in the corners of a central courtyard. This would allow the church to stay where it was and remain entirely separate from the skyscraper.But as work proceeded a number of serious errors in the engineer's calculations began to show up. To begin with, it became clear that if high winds blew on two sides of the building it could compromise the building's integrity. LeMessurier quickly recalculated in hopes of avoiding catastrophe. He was able to reach an accord with the building's primary occupant, Citibank, and avoid drawn out legal actions.Over a period of three months, teams of workers attached steel plates to reinforce the bases of all the columns. All of the work took place at night so that no one found out about the problem until twenty years later when it was revealed in an article published in *The New Yorker.*

Fortunately, the architects discovered in time that the building could collapse in a hurricane and bring neighboring buildings down with it. They were able to take measures to strengthen its foundations.

• The first space station launched by the United States had major problems right from the start. The structure called *Skylab* suffered irreversible damage on May 14, 1973. Due to oversights in the aerodynamic calculations, the station lost its anti-meteorite shield and one of its main solar panels during lift-off. This also impeded the correct functioning of the remaining solar panel, resulting in overheating and energy loss.

Skylab was the first American space station. Launched in 1973, it ran into problems during takeoff. Most of its six years in space was spent making repairs. It crashed over Australia, and NASA had to pay for damages.

Man the Lifeboats

ERROR: Everything that possibly could go wrong did.

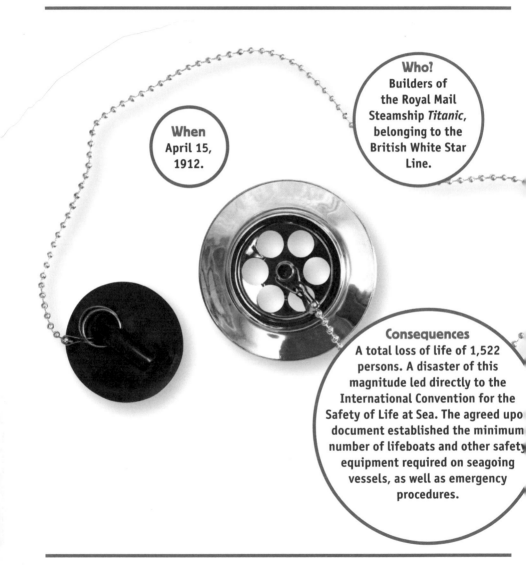

Who?
Builders of the Royal Mail Steamship *Titanic*, belonging to the British White Star Line.

When
April 15, 1912.

Consequences
A total loss of life of 1,522 persons. A disaster of this magnitude led directly to the International Convention for the Safety of Life at Sea. The agreed upon document established the minimum number of lifeboats and other safety equipment required on seagoing vessels, as well as emergency procedures.

Well boys, do your best for the women and children, and look out for yourselves.

Captain Edward John Smith (1850-1912)

The RMS *Titanic* was built by Harland and Wolff in their shipyard in Belfast in 1911. It was meant to set a standard for luxury travel.

By the end of the nineteenth century there were two companies that were competing for the lion's share of the very lucrative routes between Europe and America. One of them, the Cunard Line, relied on two ships, the *Lusitania* and the *Mauritania*. Immigration from Europe to the New World was reaching a peak at this time, and Cunard's ships carried the bulk of these passengers. But a new company was coming onto the scene, White Star Line. It planned to build three enormous ships (Olympic-class) equipped with the last word in luxury and revolutionary technology, such as watertight compartments. This system was supposed to seal the whole ship in the event that it suffered a collision and took on water. Managers and builders thought these ships would be unsinkable. Built in the shipyards of Harland and Wolff (Belfast, Northern Ireland), many design changes were introduced during

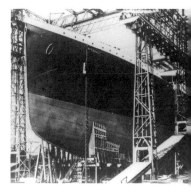

construction An additional funnel was added to the three originally planned, because it was thought that this would give the ship a more aesthetic appearance, and passengers would think that the extra funnel would provide more speed. The most important change had to do with lifeboats. The original design called for 48 lifeboats. But it was considered that so many boats would take up too much space; their number was finally reduced to only 16. A detail that cost many lives!

A luxurious engineering marvel

The naval architect Thomas Andrews, who was one of those lost at sea, was responsible for the design. The Olympic-class vessels measured more than 275 meters long, had a beam of 28 meters and a draft of 15 meters. The first vessel (the *Olympic*) was launched in 1910 and, just one year later, the brand-new *Titanic* made its first appearance. The public, critics and the press from around the world were amazed at this wonder of nautical engineering. Considered the largest and most luxurious ship of the time, it was unrivaled in luxury and elegance. Equipped with an indoor pool, a gym, a Turkish bath, a library, and four elevators, it stood as the ultimate in passenger travel. The suites were equipped with sumptuous details and very expensive pieces of furniture, including beautifully built fireplaces.

The *Titanic* embarked upon its maiden voyage from Southampton, England, the main departure point for trans-Atlantic crossings.

The first (and last) trip

This floating palace set sail on April 10, 1912. Commanded by veteran captain Edward John Smith, she left the English port of Southampton with the intention of arriving in New York in six days. All told there were 2,224 first-, second- and third-class passengers aboard the luxury ocean liner. The ship had a pleasant 24-mile journey across the Channel to reach Cherbourg, where other passengers, who reached the ship in small boats, came on board. From there she headed towards Queenstown (Ireland), crossing the Channel again and heading around the south coast of England. At 13:30 on April 11, the *Titanic* weighed anchor and left Europe, heading to New York.

Design mistakes coupled with simple bad luck led to this unforgettable disaster.

Early warnings

Everything was going smoothly with the ship holding a steady 12 knots on a calm sea. However, the radio operator did receive several warnings to stay alert of possibly dangerous ice formations in the North Atlantic. On the morning of April 14, the *Titanic* received notice from the ship *Caronia* that there were major ice shelves on the course the luxurious ship was taking. She received the same message from the Dutch ship *Noordam* and the British *Baltic*, stating that 250 miles from the position of the *Titanic* lay "large quantities of ice." Shortly after this the German ship *Amerika* warned of the presence of a "big iceberg," but this message was never relayed to the bridge by the officer in charge.

The Californian turns off the radio

Despite these repeated warnings, the *Titanic* increased

Margaret Brown, one of the *Titanic*'s survivors, presents an award to Captain Arthur Henry Rostron, captain of the *Carpathia*, which rescued stranded survivors of the wreck.

The radio operator of the *Titanic* was too busy responding to requests from important passengers to pay attention to the warnings of icebergs sent to him from other vessels.

speed and continued on a direct course to her destination. But word of impending threats kept coming. At 19:30 three consecutive notices transmitted by the British ship *Californian* referring to large icebergs were received. They indicated that the icebergs were only 50 miles from the position of the *Titanic*. At this point, the *Titanic* was making about 22 knots. Thinking it prudent to slow down, the captain discussed the possibility with the company vice president, J. Bruce Ismay. No way! The maiden voyage had to beat all records.

At 21:30, the captain retired to rest, giving orders to be awakened if there were any problems. His second-in-command ordered the lookouts to keep a careful eye on the horizon, given the repeated warnings received. Notices kept coming about icebergs, but the radio operator was busy sending messages for passengers and didn't pay them any attention. Shortly before 23:00, the *Californian*, which was about 15 miles north of the *Titanic*, changed course because of the presence of ice. The *Californian* immediately sent warnings to all vessels in the area, including the *Titanic*. But the radio operator was overwhelmed by demanding passengers and rudely replied: "Stop! You're ruining my signal. I am working." Angered by the response, the radio operator of the *Californian* decided to turn off the radio, a death sentence to most of the *Titanic's* passengers and crew.

Iceberg in sight

At 23:30, the lookouts spotted a small patch off the prow. The ship was traveling at high speed, and ten minutes later the crew realized they were headed directly towards a large iceberg. The warning was passed along to the bridge, but it was too late. Instinctively, the officer in command, William M. Murdoch, ordered that the ship tack to starboard. He put the engines into reverse and had the doors of watertight containment system shut. The giant ship began to turn but a part of the iceberg struck it and tore about 60 meters from the starboard wall under water line, ripping open five forward compartments. Oddly enough, his desperate maneuver to avoid a head-on collision had condemned the *Titanic*. In swerving away from the iceberg, he permitted the forward compartments to be breached, dooming the ship. An inspection by the ship's architect, Thomas Andrews, confirmed the worst: within two hours, the *Titanic* would rest on the bottom of the North Atlantic. The math was grim; Captain Smith estimated that many passengers were going to die for lack of lifeboats. Their total capacity was 1,178 people, while the ship was carrying 2,227 passengers and crew. In other words, 1,049 people were sentenced to death.

The visible portion of an iceberg is only a small part of its total mass, most of which is below the water line.

Rich first

The evacuation process was chaotic. Of the total places available only a little more than 700 ended up being occupied. Preference was given to the first- and second-class passengers, with the captain trying to board the women and children first. Most of the third class passengers perished.

After the collision, the chief radio operator received orders to send out telegrams asking for help. The *Californian* was relatively nearby, but refused to answer keeping radio silence due to the rudeness shown by the *Titanic*. But other ships received the notice, including the *Carpathia*, belonging to White Star's rival,

THE NEW YORK HERALD.

THE TITANIC SINKS WITH 1,800 ON BOARD; ONLY 675, MOSTLY WOMEN AND CHILDREN, SAVED

MOST APPALLING DISASTER IN MARINE HISTORY OCCURS WHEN WORLD'S LARGEST STEAMSHIP STRIKES GIGANTIC ICEBERG AT NIGHT

Front page of *The New York Herald* **the day after the accident.**

the Cunard Line, under the command of Captain Arthur Rostron. She was located about 58 miles southeast of the *Titanic*.

4,400 meters deep

By 01:15, the vessel was listing steeply and the front deck was completely covered by the cold waters of the North Atlantic (between 4 and 6 degrees C.). At 2:00 all the lifeboats had been launched, but there were still 1,500 people on the ship. Water poured in through open hatches, and the stern rose out of the sea. Now everything went dark; the ship was forced into a perpendicular position. This exposed the propellers, and the strain tore the boat apart between the third and fourth funnels. At 2:20 the middle of the bow separated from the stern and began to sink in 4,400 meters of water. The ocean swallowed the doomed passengers in a huge whirlpool. Eighty years later, the seabed is still full of unopened champagne bottles.

Victims and survivors

An hour later, the *Carpathia* launched its first flares to locate survivors and at 4:10 rescued the first lifeboat. At 5:30 news of the disaster came to the *Californian* from another ship, the *Frankfort*. A total of 710 people were rescued; the death toll was 1,522 people, killed by hypothermia or drowning. Among the victims, were the wealthy industrialists John Jacob Astor and Benjamin Guggenheim. There are no longer any living survivors of the shipwreck. The last to die was Milvina Dean, who was only 10 months old at the time. She died in England on May 31, 2009.

Although they are minor in comparison, James Cameron's film *Titanic*, is not without its own errors. For example, when the pilot decides to tack to starboard (i.e. to the right), the film shows the ship veering to the left (to port), even though we hear the people shouting "to starboard" in the background. In fact, it is said that there are more than a hundred errors in the film. For instance the Monet painting that appears in first class had not yet been painted, the Statue of Liberty is illuminated although this did not happen until 1950, hairstyles and jewelry change in the same scene, an echo is heard at sea which can't occur in open space, and Leonardo di Caprio sinks in the water when he should have floated.

The Titanic Memorial erected in Belfast in honor of the victims lost at sea.

For Want of a Hyphen

ERROR: Omission of a hyphen in the transcription of a mathematical formula for the guidance system of Mariner 1.

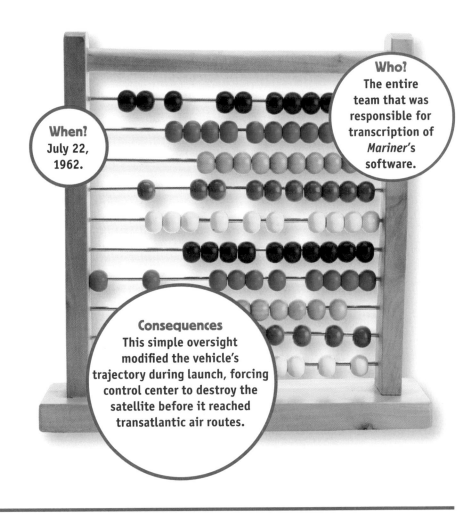

When?
July 22, 1962.

Who?
The entire team that was responsible for transcription of *Mariner's* software.

Consequences
This simple oversight modified the vehicle's trajectory during launch, forcing control center to destroy the satellite before it reached transatlantic air routes.

The history of space flight is full of oversights and blunders that have ended up costing millions of dollars and, in the worst cases, human lives. The most tragic of these occurred on the Challenger (January 28, 1986) and on the *Columbia* (February 1, 2003). In each case the lives of seven astronauts were lost. In one of the most famous events in the history of the space race the Mariner 1 probe had a starring role. Its mission was to study the planets Venus and Mercury, but it never reached its destination. In fact, it didn't even come even close, since failure during its launch caused its own destruction just five minutes after takeoff. And in this case, it was not due to a technical failure, poor design or a bad weather conditions. This multimillion-dollar mission was scrutinized down to the smallest detail by NASA's finest engineers but went to hell because of a missing hyphen.

Until Steven Spielberg's cuddly E.T., Hollywood saw aliens as frightening creatures set on world domination.

Life on Mars?

In the 1960s and 1970s, the world looked at Venus and especially Mars with some suspicion. It was believed that this mysterious planet could harbor some kind of life and its "proximity" to Earth generated concern. It did not help that a huge number of novels, TV shows and science fiction movies featured Martian invasions, and alien attacks and abductions. To fully investigate the subject NASA established the JPL (Jet Propulsion Laboratory). Located near Los Angeles, this R & D center is responsible for the design and construction of unmanned spacecraft with the aim of space exploration. Over the course of a decade (from 1962 to 1973) it built ten space probes in the Mariner

Stamp commemorating the rocket *Venera*, launched by the old Soviet Union to explore the atmosphere of Venus.

program. The program's mission was to travel to Venus, Mars and Mercury for the first time. These probes were rather small, weighing half a ton each, and were launched with the help of an Atlas rocket.

Let's see who gets there first

This was at the height of the cold war, and the space race between the United States and the Soviet Union exerted additional pressure on the engineers working on their space programs. The Russians won the first battle, sending the probe *Venera* up in 1961 to within 100,000 km of Venus, although it did not relay data to Earth. That same year, the Soviets excited the world with the launching of Yuri Gagarin, the first man in space, on April 12, 1961. NASA needed a big win. Alongside its efforts to put the first man on the moon, it started work on *Mariner 1*.

Off course

The launch of this pioneering mission was scheduled for July 22, 1962. Everything seemed fine at Cape Canaveral and the takeoff as seen from the control room was picture perfect. Suddenly, at 4 minutes and 53 seconds, the NASA team observed an unexpected tilt to the rocket. Its downward trajectory could bring it on a collision course with Trans-Atlantic shipping routes. To avoid a possible calamity, the rocket was ordered to self-destruct just six seconds before the probe was scheduled to disengage. If they had waited a little longer, the rocket could not have been destroyed.

Subsequent investigations clarified what had happened: something as simple but as fatal as a programming error. The omission of a simple hyphen in the transcription of the computer program guiding the rocket caused it to change course to compensate for the error. This failure, together with the temporary loss of contact between the satellite and the base, resulted in a very expensive failure.

Computer bugs

The scientific community has given the name "bugs" to these programming glitches. For decades, they have had programmers scratching their heads, and many have caused real disasters. In addition to the *Mariner 1* probe, here are some of the most notorious:

- The first bug that gave its name to this type of failure occurred in 1947. At that time, a team of engineers was working in a laboratory at Harvard University. Trying to determine the cause of a failure in a computer (the old Mark II, a 15-foot long monster), they discovered that a moth had slipped into the guts of the computer. The insect in question made history by literally being stuck in a logbook sheet accompanied by the following observation: "First actual case of bug being found." Hence the name "bug." Currently, the moth, with the page of annotations, is on display at the Naval Surface Warfare Center Computer Museum in Dahlgren, Virginia (USA).

- Between 1985 and 1987, defective software in the accelerator Therac-25, which is used in

Takeoff of *Mariner 1*, the first mission of the Mariner program, designed to travel to Venus. A slight error in the computer program guiding the rocket caused it to fail before leaving Earth's atmosphere.

radiation therapy, caused several cases of massive overdose of radiation (100 times the expected dose) resulting in deaths and serious injuries in medical centers in the U.S. and Canada.

We mustn't be pessimistic. Despite initial errors in the models, the *Ariane 5* rocket took off five to seven times a year and placed dozens of satellites in Earth's orbit.

- Another documented example of damage caused by poorly designed software is the explosion of the *Ariane 5* shuttle. This occurred on June 4, 1996 when, 40 seconds after the start of the launch sequence, the rocket deviated from its route. It broke in two and finally exploded. Ten years of construction and seven billion euros went into the garbage because of a bug in the software for the guidance system.

- In 1990, a malicious bug left millions of people in America unable to make international and long distance calls. The cause was a collapse in AT&T's mainframe computer. At the time AT&T was the world's biggest phone company. A bug in the software controlling the switching of long distance calls shut down its communications system. This caused such a mess that the authorities came to suspect that it was a terrorist plot.

- The Y2K bug was caused by the practice adopted by programmers of omitting the year when storing dates in electronic systems. This working method was popularized in the 60s when computers still had little memory capacity. As the new millennium approached, computer scientists began to fear that such systems could have serious difficulties when it came to recognizing the new millennium. Correcting this problem cost billions of dollars worldwide. Fortunately, it did not turn out to be the end of the world; in fact, the consequences were minimal. The

British Standards Institute promulgated Year 2000 Conformity requirements, and an international body was set up where over 200 countries could report problems encountered on January 1, 2000. The most significant incidents affected three Japanese and eight American nuclear facilities, but these adverse effects were easily contained. As the start of the new millennium neared, the apocalyptic hype increased, until the morning of January 2 dawned, and everything was just as it had always been.

Predictions of global catastrophe caused by the Y2K bug proved to be entirely unfounded. Aside from a few ripples here and there, things continued on January 1, 2000 pretty much the same as on December 31, 1999.

Tacoma Bridge Is Falling Down

ERROR: In order to achieve a more elegant and less expensive structure, the architect ignored basic principles of aerodynamics.

When?
November 7, 1940, a day with 40 m.p.h. winds.

Who?
Leon Moisseiff, chief engineer in charge of the project.

Consequences
The spectacular crash of the bridge into the Narrows River. Fortunately, there were no fatalities, except for a terrified dog who was unable to get out of a car. Following the accident ground rules were established governing the dimensions of the various bridge components and their ability to withstand high winds.

The collapse of Tacoma's suspension bridge led to major changes in bridge design.

Suspension bridges are so named because both the structure and the vehicles crossing it literally hang suspended in the air. This marvel of engineering is achieved by a carefully calculated combination of forces through a series of horizontal beams, thick cables and solid vertical towers. Their most notable feature is their flexibility. Being so long and thin, slight movements and oscillations are characteristic of this kind of construction. Everything, however, is controlled, and usually the only real problem is the shock that people can experience when crossing them in high winds.

The cheapest option

But in the case of the famous Tacoma Narrows Bridge, all this theory went to hell, or rather to the bottom of the river running below. . . Thus began the history of one of the most talked about gaffes in the history of engineering. In the early 1930s, Tacoma and Pierce counties in Washington State, decided upon the construction of a bridge across the Narrrows Strait of Puget Sound to link Tacoma and the Kitsap Peninsula. Given

A new bridge opened on October 14, 1950.

the shaky economic conditions following the Great Depression, obtaining funding was more than a little challenging.

After reviewing several designs, authorities finally decided on the cheapest option, which was presented by New York engineer Leon Moisseiff. This noted bridge engineer had established himself with his flagship project, the famous Golden Gate Bridge, a symbol of the city of San Francisco. Given his reputation, he was given carte blanche. The first thing he did was to recommend reducing the depth of support for trusses that sat beneath the roadway to stabilize it. These were originally planned to be 25-feet deep. Moisseiff proposed using more slender girders (8-foot deep). According to his design, the bridge would be thinner and more elegant, and also construction costs would be reduced. Magic words! The authorities were delighted with the proposed savings and let him follow his radical design without any real oversight.

A roller coaster

The bridge was completed on schedule. Only a few days after its opening (July 1, 1940), the problems started. The bridge was seen to buckle dangerously even under relatively benign winds. The road rose and fell alternately in certain areas of the bridge. Rocking motions were visible to drivers, drivers saw approaching cars disappear and reappear in hollows. Because of this effect, the locals ended up nicknaming the bridge "Galloping Gertie."

More than just a bridge, the Narrows Bridge became a tourist attraction. People came from all over to experience a kind of roller coaster ride. These oscillations caused a physical effect known as torsional vibration mode. Moisseiff seemed unconcerned and assured the town that the structure of the bridge was in no danger.

The collapse

Four months later, on November 7, 1940, a lateral wind of moderate intensity (about 40 miles an hour) was enough to turn the famous bridge into a giant pennant, flapping in the wind and finally breaking apart. At no time was wind resistance considered and this mistake, coupled with the problem of rigidity, finished off the Tacoma Bridge, causing it to collapse. Its spectacular destruction has been used ever since as a teaching tool in engineering courses, demonstrating the need to consider the effects of aerodynamics and resonance in the design of civil engineering structures.

Before collapsing into the river, the bridge suffered violent shaking for several hours. Finally, the central section, which weighed 11,000 tons and was 2,750 feet long, fell with a crash into the water. Its dramatic collapse was seen by many people who had come to witness the preventative closure of the bridge. A film shot by one of the travelers crossing the bridge can be seen on the internet.

Front page of a local newspaper the day after the bridge collapse shows a dramatic picture of the event.

ENVIRON-
MENT

Look at the Pretty Bunny

ERROR: Introducing 24 wild rabbits from England into a continent in which the species was not indigenous.

When?
1859.

Who?
Thomas Austin, Australian hunter and farmer.

Consequences
Since that time about 300 million rabbits have spread throughout Australia, devastating agriculture and destroying pasture land, at an annual cost of over 100 million dollars.

According to the Organization for Food and Agriculture (FAO), the invasion of rabbits in Australia has been the fastest ever recorded by a mammal in any continent. It all began in 1859 when it occurred to an enterprising Australian farmer, Thomas Austin, that breeding rabbits could be a profitable business for the settlers. So he brought 24 wild rabbits from England and started breeding them with domesticated rabbits of the same species. At first they lived in a small fenced corral in Barwon Park, southeast of Melbourne. But as we all know these animals are very sexually active and they soon outgrew their new home. Gradually they got out and, once free, began to settle on their own, creating gigantic wild colonies. Even in the worst conditions, a single female rabbit is able to give birth to four or five litters of eight per year. Multiply this figure by the thousands of feral rabbits: the impact is devastating.

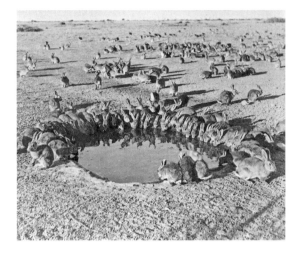

Australian authorities introduced a virulent strain of myxomatosis into the country, putting a temporary halt to the rabbit population's geometric growth.

War against the rabbit

Fed up with them, Australians declared war on the species. They began with conventional methods of population control (traps, poisons, barbed wire and release of predators). To no avail: rabbits continued with their routine, that is, eating and multiplying, eating and multiplying. . . In 1950, the authorities went to plan B: the biological control of the species by introducing the myxomatosis virus. This is an infectious disease that affects rabbits and proves fatal in just a couple of weeks. At first, the strategy seemed to work.

Tenniel's illustration from
Alice in Wonderland, showing
Alice with her companions the
Mad Hatter, the Dormouse and
the March Hare.

In two years, the rabbit population was drastically reduced from 600 to 100 million. But after a time, the rabbits became more resistant to the virus and returned to their old ways. Currently, the population of rabbits in Australia is around 300 million units and growing.

Other pests

Australians are no strangers to invasions of non-indigenous species. In the past, they have had to deal with emergencies caused by disproportionate numbers of horses, pigs, foxes, buffaloes and even frogs. Many of these species are not native and were imported for domestic work or, curiously, to control the excessive growth of other species. Currently, there are nearly two dozen vertebrate species that have been labeled as pests due to their high impact on the country's ecosystem. One is the wild camel. More than a million of these animals roam Australia and have become a real headache. These animals were introduced into Australia in 1840 for use as transport in exploring inland. It is estimated that until 1907 between 10,000 and 20,000 were imported. A first glance they seemed friendly but they have come to consume up to 80 percent of the food available in the desert. In addition, each camel can consume 200 liters of water in just 3 minutes. The authorities have launched an operation to reduce their population. . . to zero. It sounds a bit cruel, but this is the only way to control a species that could double in just under 10 years.

Invasive Species

Throughout the course of history, there are many instances of species introduced into environments that have ended up seriously damaging the ecosystem of the area. Sometimes this has been by accident, other times deliberately.
Here are some examples:

• American Mink. Imported into fur farms, some individuals escaped and today the species competes with the European mink. Members of the American species are larger, more aggressive and more adaptable. This has brought the European species to the verge of extinction.
• The Ruddy Duck. This (apparently) harmless duck has been colonizing all of Southern Europe, which has made life difficult for members of another family member, the white-headed duck.

• The Pike. This huge, voracious fish poses a threat to a number of native species, because it feeds on all kinds of fish and amphibians. It comes from Central Europe and was introduced into the Tagus River in Spain in the late 1940s.
• The Kudzu. This climbing vine native to eastern Asia and some Pacific islands was introduced into the United States in order to stop soil erosion. It competes with native plants for light. Areas infested by kudzu exhibit changes in leaf decomposition and a decrease in the amount of carbon stored in the soil.
• Zebra mussel. Originally from the Black and Caspian Seas, this mussel travels the world sticking to the hulls of ships. Their uncontrolled proliferation has caused severe and costly damage to infrastructure, interfering with all types of pipes and irrigation systems.

How to Destroy an Island

ERROR: The over-exploitation of the island of Nauru's natural wealth of phosphate has ruined its environment.

When?
1903-1990.

Who?
Different mineral-extracting companies and spendthrift island governments.

Consequences
Desertification of the island, exhaustion of resources, and economic collapse.

In the early twentieth century, Nauru was a small paradise lost in the Pacific. This
beautiful island surrounded
by reefs had a valuable mineral as its own treasure: guano.
For centuries, millions of mi-
gratory birds had deposited
their droppings on its surface. Over the millennia, these
remains were transformed
into agricultural phosphate of
the highest quality that would
bring fortune (and misfortune) to the locals.

Attracted by such a goose
laying golden eggs, mining
companies from all over the
world came to Nauru. During

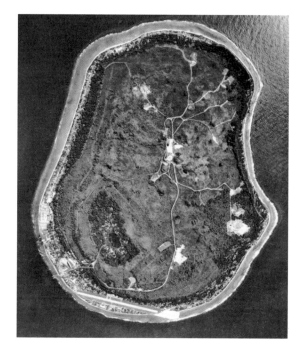

Satellite view of the island
of Nauru.

the following decades, they harvested more than six
million tons of phosphates. There seemed to be no
end to the riches and the Nauruans became a kind of
emirs of the Pacific, thanks to their unique and profitable natural resource. Although the phosphate constituted almost the only resource of the island, it
nonetheless assured Nauruans very high living standards for several decades. There was no unemployment, workers did not pay taxes and social services
were completely free. The very high income turned
the island into one of the countries with the highest per capita income in the world. But it still wanted more. With the aim of boosting its economy, Nauru became a fiscal paradise in the 1990s.

Above: A plant processing phosphates. **Below:** Direct effect of overexploitation. Phosphates are used in organic farming and processed for conventional farming. Currently their use is in decline.

Bankruptcy

The intensity of the phosphate extractions gradually exhausted its supply. Scraped to the bone, the ecosystem of the island was irreversibly degraded. Currently, 90 percent of the central part of the island is a non-cultivable desert plateau, which further limits the resources that the country possesses. 80 percent of Nauru has been completely devastated. Wherever you go you come across a barren terrain of jagged limestone pinnacles. In addition, intensive mining has had a strong adverse impact on marine life, which has been reduced by 40 percent. According to official reports, the island's government currently has no funds for the management of basic public services. Unsound financial management and lack of attention to the development of alternative sources of wealth have led to an untenable situation. At the time of this writing Nauru has the worst rate of deflation in the world, standing at minus 3.6 percent. Over the last few years, the possibilities of economic diversification have been seriously hampered by missing or completely mortgaged assets. Currently, the economy is in transition to the post-phosphate era. The growth potential is limited given their low agricultural productivity and services.

With its ruined environment, Nauru has neither arable land nor water resources. It is entirely dependent on

Town of Arenibek on Nauru in 1896, before exploitation destroyed the island's environment. Before business interests took over, it was a pristine island paradise.

Australia for food. Its lack of natural harbors means that the provisions need to be transported by air, or by sea, anchoring offshore and then brought to the island in small boats.

Greed is not so good

The search for cheap oil and its transportation from wells to refineries has caused many ecological disasters of gigantic proportions, often because of errors that could have been avoided. Many of these were aggravated by the place and circumstances under which they occurred; for example, one of the largest spills occurred in the Persian Gulf in 1991, during the first Gulf War. No less than 4,000,000 barrels of oil were spilled, compared to 400,000 from the Exxon Valdez in Alaska in 1989. It is estimated that the spill of the Deepwater Horizon rig in the Gulf of Mexico in 2010 amounted to 5,000,000 barrels. In this incident, miscalculations and negligence caused an explosion while drilling a well on the sea floor. Eleven people were killed, the platform caught fire, and the flow of oil from the burst pipe could not be stopped. Accident management teams made one mistake after another.

The Day the Big Wave Hit

ERROR: Not having a warning system that covered the Indian Ocean to provide advanced warning of tidal waves.

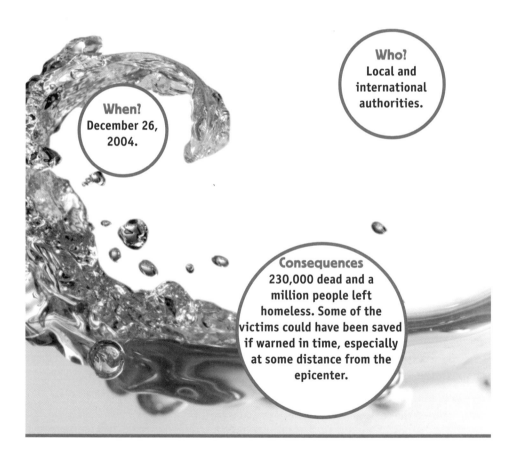

When?
December 26, 2004.

Who?
Local and international authorities.

Consequences
230,000 dead and a million people left homeless. Some of the victims could have been saved if warned in time, especially at some distance from the epicenter.

We all remember the terrible destruction inflicted by the Indian Ocean tsunami at the end of 2004. The death toll was horrific. Hundreds of thousands of survivors were left injured and exposed to disease. Poor communities were thrust deeper into poverty.

Sálvano Briceño, Director UN secretariat of the International Strategy for Disaster Reduction

A few minutes before eight o'clock on the morning of December 26, 2004, a very strong undersea earthquake with its epicenter west of Sumatra (Indonesia) caused a tsunami of devastating proportions. The earthquake triggered a series of immense tidal waves along the coasts of countries bordering the Indian Ocean. Within hours there were 230,000 killed and thousands of people on the coasts of Asia and East Africa displaced or rendered homeless. Waves up to 100 feet high swept over Indonesia; the blast of giant waves reached Thailand, Sri Lanka and Indian islands such as Andaman and Nicobar. Six hours later, the waves reached the African coast of Somalia and Kenya. This Asian tsunami had become one of the deadliest natural disasters in modern history.

In the last decades, population growth along coastlines has led to a danger of major losses from flooding and other severe weather conditions.

No warning system

The death toll was particularly high because it was the first time in over 100 years that a tsunami in the Indian Ocean affected the coasts, hitting countries that were unprepared for it. Although it is impossible to fully protect

The tsunami that ravaged coastlines and islands was closely followed by worldwide media.

coastal areas from the impact of a tsunami, precautions can be taken that can greatly lower the risks. In this case people were left entirely on their own, due largely to the absence of warning systems in the Indian Ocean. While the countries bordering the Pacific were equipped with a system of buoys that warned of arriving tsunamis, there was nothing comparable in the Indian Ocean. There, systems were in place to warn of monsoons and tropical cyclones, but no warning system for tsunamis existed.

Because of better information, public education and networks that provide advance notice, large tsunamis in recent decades have caused fewer casualties among the coastal Pacific population. The UN spent years insisting on the need to launch a warning network in the Indian Ocean and other areas of the planet where a large percentage of the population lives along the coast.

Joining with the UN have been environmentalists from different specialties. They noted that, among other things, the death of coral reefs due to climate change and the cutting of mangroves for farming prawns and shrimp have increased the effects of tsunamis. According to experts, it seems that coastal mangrove forests, together with healthy barrier reefs, could have had a braking effect on the giant wave, which in some places reached a height of 36 feet.

Even the best warning system might not have helped the people of Indonesia, as the giant wave descended upon them in a few minutes. But in countries like Sri Lanka and India, the tsunami took almost two hours to make an appearance. A good prevention system could have alerted the population to evacuate threatened areas.

View of the devastation caused by the tsunami on Sumatra. The tsunami of 2004 was the most destructive in history, claiming the lives of 230,000 people.

In the aftermath

In October 2009 the first successful simulation of alert against a full-scale tsunami in the Indian Ocean was tested. The test involved 18 countries bordering the Indian Ocean. The project evaluated the Indian Ocean Tsunami Warning System (IOTWS), established by the Intergovernmental Oceanographic Commission (IOC) of UNESCO. This system is composed of seismographic systems employing networks of tide gauges that transmit data in real time, as well as pressure sensors in deep water and national warning centers linked to national disaster management systems. Since its inception the system has provided advance notice of several possible tsunamis allowing proper safety precautions to be taken.

TO ERR IS HUMAN

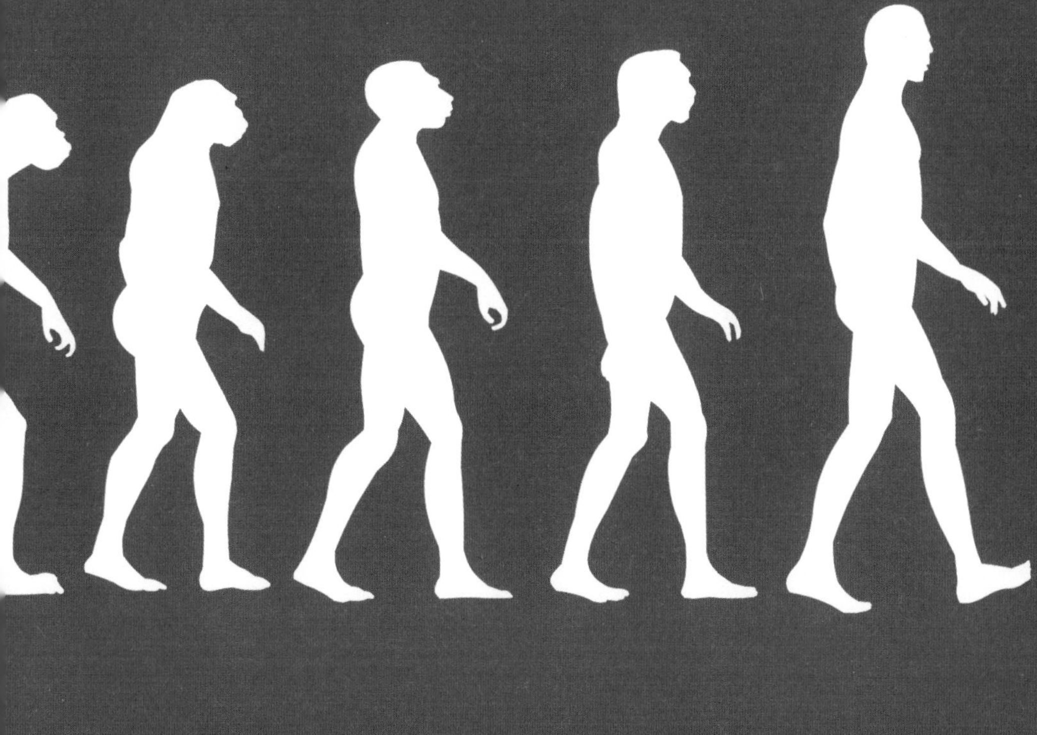

Port or Starboard?

ERROR: A series of mistakes in navigation and the miscalculation of relative position on the part of the two ships.

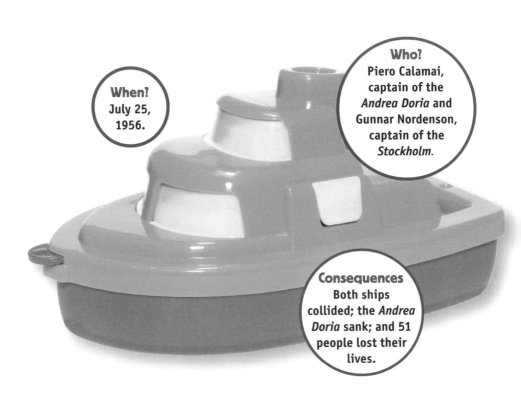

When?
July 25, 1956.

Who?
Piero Calamai, captain of the *Andrea Doria* and Gunnar Nordenson, captain of the *Stockholm.*

Consequences
Both ships collided; the *Andrea Doria* sank; and 51 people lost their lives.

At the end of the 1940s, Italy wanted to demonstrate to the world its economic and social development. In order to accomplish this, the Italian shipping company Società di Navigazione commissioned the Ansaldo shipyards (in Sestri Ponente) to build two ships that would represent its achievements. The finished products were two splendid ships: the *Andrea Doria* and *Christoforo Colombo*, named in honor of the two most illustrious Genovese natives in nautical history. The first was launched on June 10, 1951. It measured 212 meters long and weighing nearly 30,000 tons. With the capacity to accommodate more than 1,200 passengers, it was replete with luxurious period details. There were three outdoor pools (one for each class), three cinemas and several first-class suites. But in addition to its grand appearance, it was equipped with the latest in navigation technology and a hull with eleven watertight compartments rendering the vessel "unsinkable." Or so her captain, the veteran Piero Calamai, thought until the evening of 25 July, 1956. That day, the *Andrea Doria* was heading west about 160 miles from the port of New York and was approaching the lighthouse of Nantucket. The officer on deck decided to pass the lighthouse on the port side. This maneuver was very common for ships heading both to and from New York. And that was the course taken by the passenger ship *Stockholm* of the Swedish-American Line. Its captain Gunnar Nordenson had sailed from New York shortly before noon destined for the Swedish city of Gothenburg. His boat was smaller, but the bow was heavily reinforced to cope with the ice often encountered on its transatlantic voyages. Its length measured 160 meters and it had room for 800 passengers.

The sea god Neptune claimed his tribute on the night of July 25, 1956.

Course changes

At about 9:00 P.M., the Swedish captain ordered a change of course of three degrees to port, to bring the ship closer to the Nantucket Lighthouse. Both ships were following their usual route on a well-known course. Shortly before 11:00 P.M., the bridge of the *Andrea Doria* observed the signal of an approaching vessel four degrees to starboard at a distance of about 17 miles. Initially, Calamai estimated that both ships would pass safely starboard to starboard. International rules dictate that "when two power-driven vessels approach head-on, from opposite or nearly opposite directions, and there exists a danger of collision, passing should be port to starboard." The captain saw that the distance between the two ships was narrowing and ordered a course change of four degrees to port.

Collision

Around 11:00 P.M., the *Andrea Doria* was traveling through an area of dense fog and poor visibility. Another navigation rule states that in such circumstances "ships shall reduce speed." Indeed, Captain Calamai ordered the ship to slow down, but it still maintained a speed of over 21 knots. Meanwhile, the *Stockholm's* radar had detected the presence of the *Andrea Doria*. The Swedes were navigating through the fog as well and posted a watch on the port side to guard against the dangerous proximity of the approaching ship. Suddenly the Swedish sailor on guard shouted "Lights to port!" The ships were too close together, and the *Stockholm* quickly ordered a 20 degree turn to starboard, thinking that this would widen the distance. But it actually brought them closer together. The *Stockholm* reversed its engines, trying to stop. Meanwhile, the *Andrea Doria* engaged in a hard turn to port attempting to get past the other ship. There was, however, not enough

The *Andrea Doria* an Italian vessel, was the largest ship of its time. Launched in 1951, it boasted the very latest luxuries. It had three swimming pools and the cabins were decorated with works of art. In contrast, the *Stockholm* out of Sweden was the smallest cruise ship operating in the Atlantic at that time.

time to perform the maneuver and prevent the disaster. At about quarter past 11:00 P.M., the ships collided, with the reinforced bow of the *Stockholm* striking the starboard side of the *Andrea Doria*. The collision caused a gaping hole almost 30 meters in diameter in the side of the Italian vessel. It began listing to around 20 degrees to starboard, filling five fuel tanks with thousands of tons of inrushing water. This added to the problem. Slowly, the ship began to sink.

51 victims

The proximity to the coast and a large number of boats in the area made it possible to rescue most of the passengers and crew within a few hours. Between the two ships there were 1,705 people on board. Of these 51 died, 5 from the *Stockholm* and 46 from the *Andrea Doria*. Today the Italian ship lies at a depth of 90 meters on a flat sandbank lying at an angle of 22 degrees to starboard, hiding the hole made by the *Stockholm*. Every year it is visited by hundreds of divers, although over the years the ship's structure has been seriously compromised.

Nantucket Lighthouse was the last light seen by the *Andrea Doria* before it sank.

Not Ready for Takeoff

ERROR: To take off without first getting permission from the control tower.

When?
March 27, 1977.

Consequences
The terrible collision cost 583 lives. In its aftermath a series of regulations were put into effect by international bodies. From that point onwards all flight control towers use standard English terminology and automatic navigation systems have been installed on all airplanes. Ground radar, which only existed in big cities such as New York, London and Paris, have now been installed in most airports around the world.

Who?
Jacob Van Zanten, captain of KLM flight #4805 and Victor Grubbs, captain of PAA flight #1736, responsible for the one of the worst accidents in the history of aviation.

Representation of the collision between two Boeing 747s at Los Rodeos Airport on Tenerife in the Canary Islands.

Human error has been the principal cause of plane crashes. This was the case with the tragic accident at Los Rodeos, the airport in Tenerife (one of the Canary Islands), between two Boeing 747s, one KLM and the other Pan Am. Both flights had been diverted from the original destination of Gran Canaria Airport on the Canary island of Gran Canaria. The KLM was a charter flight leaving from Schiphol Airport in Amsterdam. The Pan Am flight originated in Los Angeles.

The misfortune began to take shape when a bomb exploded in the passenger terminal of the Gran Canaria Airport. The bomb had been planted by a separatist movement, the anti-Francoist Fuerzas Armadas Guanches.

A second bomb threat caused the airport to temporarily close, and both flights were diverted to Los Rodeos, on the neighboring island of Tenerife. At that time, the Tenerife airport was too small to support international air traffic. It employed only two air traffic controllers and did not have ground radar.

Cockpit of a Boeing 747.
Despite the impressive array of technological devices and monitors the final responsibility is in the hands of the pilot.

Two serious errors

The closing in Gran Canaria lasted a few hours, and then the airport was finally reopened. The American aircraft requested permission to continue on to its destination, but it could not do so at the moment, because the KLM plane was blocking the runway. In fact, both flights had been instructed to move to the same runway, because of the congestion from the diversion of flights from Gran Canaria. The Dutch flight had just refueled, its tanks filled with 15,000 gallons of fuel, when it received permission to proceed for takeoff. Meanwhile, Victor Grubbs, the Pan Am pilot, was instructed to follow the KLM flight down the runway and take the third exit left and take off on a parallel runway. The airport was experiencing dense fog conditions and it may well have been for this reason that the Pan Am rolled past the third exit and continued onto the fourth. The American pilot continued to report his position to the control tower as did the Dutch flight. The KLM pilot, however, was growing impatient and informed the tower that he was about to take off. The captain could not see that the Pan Am flight was on the same runway, nor could the air traffic controllers in the tower, because of the fog. Then a second fatal error occurred: due to a misunderstanding or poor sound quality in communications, the KLM plane accelerated and took off, despite the fact that the tower had not yet authorized takeoff. Thirteen seconds later (at 17:06 P.M.) it collided with the American plane at a speed of 270 mph. The crash tore the roof of the cab and the upper passenger deck of the Pan Am plane and its tail was

The investigation

Spanish, Dutch and American investigators concluded that in addition to the existence of the fog, the KLM pilot did not receive proper clearance for takeoff, possibly because he was concerned about complying with KLM's duty-time rules as well as with deteriorating weather conditions. There were also communication errors between the aircraft and the control tower, and Los Rodeos was congested by the rerouting of flights from Gran Canaria due to the bomb explosion.

hit by the Dutch aircraft's engines. It traveled 150 meters and hit the ground, sliding for another 300 meters, engulfed in flames. All 248 people aboard the KLM died in the fire as well as 335 of the 380 people aboard the Pan Am. Subsequently, experts estimated that if there had been an additional 25 feet between the two planes disaster would have been averted. That is, the difference of a few seconds might have avoided one of the worst tragedies, if not the worst, in the history of civil aviation.

Statistically traveling by air is much safer than by car. But the spectacular nature of airplane accidents and their high cost in human lives makes them the subject of media attention.

Midnight in Bhopal

ERROR: Contracting out to unqualified people risk prevention measures in a chemical plant in Bhopal, India.

When?
December 3, 1984.

Who?
The American multinational corporation Union Carbide.

Consequences
The chemical leak caused the immediate deaths of 3,000 people. Between 7,000 and 10,000 more died within the next few days; and at least an additional 15,000 deaths in the succeeding years have been attributed to the disaster.

During the 1950s insect infestations ravaged crops world-wide. Farmers had few weapons to deal with them. The most commonly used pesticide was DDT, but many countries began to ban its use because of its high toxicity and the damage it caused to animal life. There was an urgent need to find a suitable replacement. Of the companies searching for the silver bullet, the Union Carbide Corporation, with 130 subsidiaries in 40 countries, and the third largest chemical company in the U.S., was playing a leading role.

After years of work a team of chemists and entomologists hit upon a solution. They created Sevin, an economic pesticide that proved effective against most pests, and best of all completely harmless to humans and the environment. There was just one caveat. Its manufacture called for the use of highly toxic substances such as methylamine and phosgene gas. The combination of these gases produces methyl isocyanate (MIC), one of the most unstable and dangerous of all chemical compounds. Laboratory tests on animals showed that a miniscule amount caused total respiratory collapse, irreversible blindness and terrible chemical burns on the skin. But business is business, and since the pesticide had the potential to benefit millions, the patent holders could monopolize a vast market and put an end to infestations worldwide.

From heaven to hell

In 1967, Union Carbide settled in India and began producing the Sevin in a small factory in Bhopal, in the state of Madhya Pradesh. Demand for pesticides increased dramatically and the Indian Ministry of Agriculture granted the U.S. company permission to produce 5,000 tons of pesticide. Due to strong demand, at first the rate of production was extremely high. But the ini-

The manufacture of pesticides is highly dangerous because of the toxicity of the various components that are used.

Ruins of the Union Carbide plant in Bhopal. Chemical companies often move their factories to countries where there are fewer regulations. **and less oversight.**

tial euphoria began to fade and by the mid-1970s, production fell by half. The company started to lose money. As a result, Union Carbide instituted cutbacks. It laid off more than half its workforce. Most of those forced to leave were technicians and highly skilled—and highly paid—workers. Their functions were assigned to unskilled workers with little or no knowledge of chemistry or safety precautions. In addition, the amount of money spent in maintaining the plant was drastically reduced. Insufficient attention was paid to the risks that these policies posed to plant safety.

A fatal mistake

Things were going from bad to worse. In the summer of 1984, the factory closed down and was subsequently decommissioned. Now we come to the night of the disaster. At 12:30 in the morning of December 3, 1984, the Union Carbide plant was completely inactive. Most of the valves and lines were in poor condition and safety systems were non-functional. Only a few workers were at work, cleaning methyl isocyanate out of the pipes with pressurized water. The injected water circulating through the pipes at high pressure brought in all kinds of impurities and caused a runaway reaction. Tragically the pipes began to leak and contaminated water entered the inside of a tank containing 42 tons of unstable methyl isocyanate. In just seconds, the mixture caused a backlash in the form of toxic gas. Two geysers of poison gas were projected instantly skywards toward Bhopal.

Bhopal is a city of about 1,000,000 inhabitants in central India.

A paltry compensation

A series of accusations and lawsuits followed the accident. Finally, Union Carbide acknowledged that the Bhopal plant did not have sufficient safety measures. It also came to light that people hired for the cleanup were unqualified. The U.S. multinational tried to accuse some of its employees of sabotage, but eventually had to admit their direct responsibility for the disaster. Finally, Union Carbide Corporation came to an agreement with the Indian government. Compensation for damages amounted to $470 million, but this figure was only one sixth the amount the plaintiffs had requested.

The Bhopal tragedy was the world's worst industrial accident. The photograph shows a demonstration demanding the extradition of Union Carbide's president, William Anderson.

Getting away with murder

There are still an estimated 300 tons of toxic waste in the affected area. Another 10,000 tons of toxic waste still lies buried near the factory. More than 100,000 people continue to suffer health problems caused by the thousands of tons of toxic gas that were released into the area. The company responsible for the accident left the factory and 16 years later was bought by Dow Chemical, which refuses to take any responsibility, despite the fact that children are still being born blind from its after effects. Compensation to victims of Bhopal is limited, for the moment, by the agreement Union Carbide reached with the Indian government in 1989: $470 million dollars, a figure grossly inadequate to pay for the loss of life and the continuing ill health of the people of Bhopal.

This Is Just a Test

ERROR: To ignore safety regulations, causing the worst accident in the history of nuclear power.

When?
April 26, 1986.

Who?
Those in charge of administering and operating the nuclear power plant at Chernobyl.

Consequences
According to the Union of Concerned Scientists the accident caused 4,000 deaths, including those of 50 first responders and 3,950 victims of radiation sickness. There were mass evacuations and the area around the plant remains contaminated to this day.

For the first time ever we encountered in reality such a sinister force as nuclear energy that has escaped control.

From a speech by Mikhail Gorbachev following the disaster

There was one error after another. The workers lacked proper training and never understood the dangerous nature of their actions. The test that caused the accident was to have been done during the day, when the most experienced engineers were at work. But this would have meant an interruption of the power supply to Kiev. So the test was put off until nighttime, when energy demand on the ground was lower. By then, the scientists in charge of the reactor had gone home. Only a young and inexperienced team was in charge of reactor No. 4. Within the first ten days after the explosion, radioactive contamination spread over 77,000 square miles. Even today, mushrooms, berries and wildlife show high levels of the cesium that has poisoned the forests and mountains of the region.

Testing, testing...

At 1:23 A.M. on April 26, 1986, there was a catastrophe without precedent in the history of industrialization. The reactor No. 4 of the Chernobyl nuclear power plant suffered a serious accident that caused the graphite monitor of the reactor to catch fire, releasing tons of highly radioactive materials into the atmosphere: an amount

The use of nuclear power as a source of energy has been the subject of much debate. It is a cleaner source than carbon, but the potential consequences of accidents are much greater.

200 times that of both atomic bombs dropped on Hiroshima and Nagasaki in 1945.

The Chernobyl nuclear plant is located about 70 miles north of the Ukrainian capital of Kiev. It had four reactors that could produce 1,000 megawatts each when operating at full capacity. However, their design was somewhat outdated and no longer met the safety requirements that were imposed in the West on all nuclear reactors for civilian use. One of Chernobyl's most serious shortcomings was that the plant had no containment facility, a concrete and steel structure whose function is to contain a possible leak of radioactive gases. Because of this and other concerns about safety measures, the plant manager decided to do tests with the intention of increasing the outmoded security of the installation. It was known that the plant would not be safe for 60–75 seconds after total loss of electric power, and the test was designed to change the switching sequences. The staff began to cut the power output of the reactor with the turbine generator running at full speed. Then the generator was to be shut off to check how long it would continue generating electricity. In case of failure, the emergency coolant pumps require minimal power to get started, and the plant technicians wanted to make sure that it could provide the bridging power for coolant pumps until the emergency generators were up and running. As part of the preparations, some very important monitoring systems were disabled, including the automatic safety shutdown mechanism. It is known that at least six safety regulations were violated during the test.

Xenon poisoning

Three workers were in charge of this potentially dangerous test: Boris Stolyarchuck, who controlled the pumps of pressurized water: Yuri Korneev, in charge of the turbines, and Leonid Toptunov, a young and fairly inexperienced engineer, who was responsible for the control rods of the reactor. The operating sequence was complex and difficult for a neophyte. In short, what happened was this:

Reducing reactor power can lead to a dangerous phenomenon known as reactor poisoning. Several protection systems, such as emergency cooling and power regulation, had been disconnected. So, to prevent collapse of the reactor, operators manually removed several rods to restore power. With the reactor about to go, Toptunov withdrew too many rods. Safety rules have always required a minimum of 30 rods in the reactor and this time there were only 18 left. With the emergency systems disconnected,

Photo of one of the first responders at Chernobyl. Their heroism limited the terrible damage of the breach.

One of the helicopters that helped dampen the flames.

This collapsed building is eloquent testimony to the environmental and human destruction in Chernobyl's dead zone.

the reactor underwent an extremely fast rise in power that the operators did not detect in time. A cloud of hydrogen began to form within the core, causing the first explosion. At 1:23 AM, this explosion blew apart the steel roof of the reactor, causing a fire in the plant and a gigantic emission of radioactive material into the atmosphere. Outside air entered the reactor and the gas mixture caused a second explosion.

Radioactive graveyard

Following the accident at Chernobyl, work was begun on building a structure called a sarcophagus, to protect the reactor by isolating it from the outside. But with the passage of time, the structure became degraded from the effects of radiation, heat and the corrosive materials generated. There was a serious risk of a meltdown and scientists urged that the structure be strengthened. Ukraine, unable to obtain the necessary financing in the short time available, asked for international help. Finally, the construction of a second sarcophagus was completed. It is supposed to prevent possible radioactive leaks for at least 100 years.

Evacuation

According to official reports, more than 180 tons of nuclear reactor fuel — enriched uranium — were blown into the atmosphere. Firefighters and workers tried from the very beginning to seal off the reactor and prevent the escape of radioactive materials. Their unsuccessful efforts came at the cost of their own lives. Exposed to the atmosphere, the graphite core burned violently, with the temperature reaching 2,500 degrees C. and radioactive smoke spreading throughout the surrounding area. Subsequently, the authorities began to organize the evacuation of the nearby population. They started in the city of Pripyat (founded in 1970 specifically to house workers at the plant) and continued for days afterwards moving residents within 20 miles of the site. To prevent the continuing release of emissions, a group of army helicopters doused the core with a mixture of neutron-absorbing materials with the intent of preventing a chain reaction.

Medals awarded posthumously to first responders.

The Challenger Disaster

ERROR: Ignoring the repeated admonishments of engineers, who warned about the possible failure of the seals responsible for ensuring the integrity of the rockets. These seals broke when exposed to freezing temperatures on the morning prior to the launch of the Challenger.

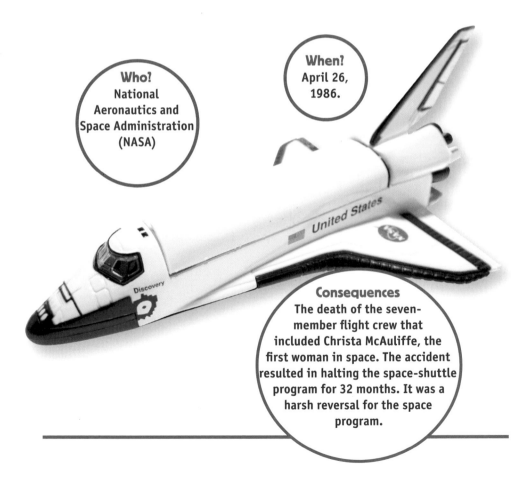

Who?
National Aeronautics and Space Administration (NASA)

When?
April 26, 1986.

Consequences
The death of the seven-member flight crew that included Christa McAuliffe, the first woman in space. The accident resulted in halting the space-shuttle program for 32 months. It was a harsh reversal for the space program.

For a successful technology, reality must take precedence over public relations, for nature cannot be fooled.

Richard P. Feynman, physicist and member of the Rogers Commission, which investigated the disaster.

The crew of the *Challenger*. From left to right, back row: Ellison S. Onizuka, Sharon Christa McAuliffe, Greg Jarvis and Judy Resnik; seated, Michael J. Smith, Dick Scobee and Ron McNair.

In the mid-1980s, the U.S. space program was betting big on space shuttles. According to NASA, they were much cheaper than conventional rockets and would further the ultimate dream of building a space station. Another of their great virtues was the ability to put satellites into orbit and bring them back to Earth .

During the years of research that preceded the launch of this aircraft, engineers encountered several obstacles. The most important task was to find the ideal booster.

Flight of the *Challenger* in 1983. This shuttle was the workhorse of the shuttle program. It transported supplies to *Spacelab*, the American space station.

Finally NASA decided upon two Solid Rocket Boosters (SRB) instead of one.

O-Rings

Four companies competed for the contract to build the shuttle's boosters. Finally, Morton Thiokol Company gained the upper hand. Their design, however, had one drawback: the fuel was divided into segments and had a risk of leakage. That was unacceptable, so Thiokol engineers created devices called O-rings to seal the joints between the segments. Once this workaround was tested, it was found to have serious flaws. For example, a water pressure test showed that fluid could pass through the joints (that were supposed to be hermetically sealed) due to the phenomenon of joint rotation. In an actual launch, it would leak gases generated by the rockets, and gas circulation could erode the ring to a point at which it could no longer be relied on. Subsequent tests continued to show the failure of the O-rings, but that was not enough to halt flights.

Satellites in orbit

The shuttle *Challenger* was important in ushering in the new era of communication satellites. In the early 1980s, the *Challenger* participated in several STS (Space Transportation System) program missions. The vehicles were designed to make about 100 flights. In 1986, the *Challenger* was assigned a new mission: to orbit the TDRS-B satellite and Spartan-Halley. The latter was a kind of astronomical platform that the shuttle would launch into orbit to take astronomical observations for a few days. Then the platform was supposed to be recovered and returned to ground. The Spartan was launched to study Halley's comet, which at that time was on one of its periodic visits to Earth. In addition, the mission

also had a public relations dimension. The teacher Christa McAuliffe was enlisted to give science lessons from space.

The *Challenger* seen through the clouds at the John F. Kennedy Space Center on Cape Canaveral.

Doubts on the eve of launch

The mission was christened STS-51-L, and initially planned for takeoff on January 22, 1986. The expedition suffered seven delays for various reasons (such as technical problems and weather) until the new launch date was fixed for January 28. But not all the signs were good. Just a day earlier, a team of engineers from Morton Thiokol held a teleconference with NASA managers to assess the launch. A number of them were still concerned about the performance of the famous O-rings.

They had proven that they could become dangerously eroded when the ambient temperature during takeoff was below 11.7 degrees C. The night before the launch, the mercury was expected to fall to -2 degrees C. , and therefore it was risky to go ahead with the mission. However, Morton Thiokol management ignored these warnings and decided to continue the mission with the blessing of NASA. Overnight, ice began to form on the launch pad at Kennedy Space Center in Florida. In those conditions, it was very risky to hold the launch. In fact, for safety reasons, the shuttle could not be launched at temperatures below 0 degrees C. In the morning and after several inspections, it was found that the ice was melting, and the launch time was set for 11:38 A.M.

The *Challenger* exploded on its tenth mission. The cabin remained intact but broke apart when it crashed into the ocean.

Accident televised

At the moment of takeoff, the hot gases of the right rocket began to escape. As the Thiokol engineers had feared, the O-rings were not properly sealing the fuel compartments. The erosion caused by the flow of gas led to a breach in the adjacent SRB joint and freed large amounts of hydrogen and oxygen. Within seconds their reaction produced an explosion. The pilots lost control, and the shuttle, exposed to severe aerodynamic conditions, broke into several pieces. The crew had no chance to escape. Two minutes and 45 seconds after the explosion, the cabin crashed into the Atlantic Ocean at about 200 mph from a height of 10,000 feet. This all happened as CNN was broadcasting the launch live to the whole country. The impact was tremendous and would only be surpassed years later by the destruction of the Twin Towers. After the accident, the Rogers Commission Report determined that the cause of the fault had, indeed, been the malfunction of the O-rings. NASA shouldered the blame, redesigned the shuttle (especially the rockets) and reduced the number of flights per year. But they did not seem to have done their homework: years afterward similar criticisms were heard after the crash of another shuttle, the *Columbia*, on February 1, 2003.

Crew of the *Columbia*, the second shuttle disaster, this time in 2003. It broke up during reentry. All of the crew perished.

Loss of the *Columbia*

The *Challenger* was not the only space shuttle lost during a mission. On February 1, 2003, the space shuttle *Columbia*, during the STS-107 mission, was destroyed upon reentry into the atmosphere after spending 15 days in space. Part of the heat shield had been lost during launch, and this caused a wing to overheat on its return to Earth. All seven crew members perished.

Fatal Errors (or Dumb Deaths)

No one wants to die, but even worse is to die out of sheer stupidity. Whether by bad luck, inability or imprudence, many people have gone to the next world in the dumbest way possible, many more than we can imagine. So many that, in 1985, the Darwin Awards were born. These are awarded (posthumously, of course) to an individual or individuals who die from carelessness or error. Although there is some irony and humor to the awards, the organization takes them very seriously and has established a list of criteria for candidates:

- The candidate must be dead.
- Death must be caused by an astonishing lack of good sense.
- Death must be caused by one's own idiocy, not by the agency of someone else.
- The candidate must have been of sound mind at the time of death.
- The event must be verified.

In the words of its creator, the molecular biologist Wendy Northcutt:

In the spirit of Charles Darwin, the Darwin Awards commemorate individuals who protect our gene pool by making the ultimate sacrifice of their own lives. Darwin Award winners eliminate themselves in an extraordinarily idiotic manner, thereby improving our species' chances of long-term survival.

Most winners are anonymous people whose deaths have been brought to the attention of the committee over

the years. But if we look through the pages of history, we also find a few personalities who ended their days in moronic ways. The following are some notable examples.

Aeschylus (525–456 B.C.)

Considered to be the founder of Greek tragedy with plays such as *The Persians*, *The Oresteia*, and *Seven against Thebes*, Aeschylus died in an extremely theatrical fashion. Warned by an oracle that he would be crushed by the roof of a house, he decided to move out of town to somewhere that there was less chance of that happening. Unfortunately, he died soon after, having been hit in the head by a tortoise shell dropped by a vulture.

Archimedes of Syracuse (287–212 B.C.)

Perhaps the greatest Greek mathematician as well as an inventor, physicist, astronomer and engineer, his contributions to science include advances in hydrostatics and statics and the explanation of the principle behind the lever. He is also recognized as inventing and designing innovative machinery, including siege engines and the famous Archimedes screw. He died during the Second Punic War when Roman forces under General Marcus Claudius Marcellus captured the city of Syracuse after a siege of two years. According to Plutarch's account, Marcellus was an admirer of Archimedes and ordered that the famous mathematician be brought to him. A Roman soldier came to his house to escort him back to the general. Archimedes, however, was deep in contemplation of a mathematical problem and told the soldier not to bother him. Affronted by this lack of respect, the soldier drew his sword and dispatched him without further ado.

Domenico Fetti, *Archimedes*.
One of the greatest thinkers of the classical age, Archimedes was slain by an impatient Roman soldier.

Attila the Hun (406–453)

The last and most fearsome general of the Huns conquered a large part of Europe. Known in the West as the "Scourge of God," his possessions extended from Central Europe to the Black Sea, and from the Danube to the Baltic Sea. This universally feared warrior died from a nosebleed on the last of his many wedding nights. (His last bride was a beautiful young woman named Ildico).

Jean-Baptiste Lully (1632–1687)

Lully was the court composer to Louis XIV and responsible for introducing opera to France. His great influence on the music of the era came to an end because of a self-inflicted wound from his conducting staff. This was before there were hand-held batons. At that time conductors hit the ground with a heavy rod. Apparently, his foot got in the way. The wound became infected and eventually gangrenous. He flatly refused to have the infected limb amputated, because he didn't want to give up dancing. This led to a slow and painful death.

Attila and his brother Bleda. Bleda died in a suspicious accident while hunting with his brother. Attila succumbed to a nosebleed. The painting is attributed to Tamás Tulipan.

King Adolphus Frederick of Sweden (1710–1771)

Who says that folks don't eat well in northern Europe. This Swedish monarch was certainly not of that opinion, when at the age of 61 he regaled himself with a dinner of lobster, caviar, choucroute, chicken soup, smoked venison, champagne and fourteen desserts. He died a few days later from serious digestive problems.

Isadora Duncan (1878–1927)

The curious death of the great American ballerina served to enhance her legendary status. On September 14, 1927, Duncan was riding in a car with a friend when her long scarf got caught in one of the rear wheels and strangled her. The next morning, the following obituary appeared

Above: Isadora Duncan in 1910. The great ballerina died in a cruel and absurd automobile accident **Below:** Harry Houdini died because of a ridiculous bet he made with some college students.

in The New York Times: "Isadora Duncan, the American dancer, tonight met a tragic death at Nice on the Riviera. According to dispatches from Nice, Miss Duncan was hurled in an extraordinary manner from an open automobile in which she was riding and instantly killed by the force of her fall to the stone pavement." Another account says she was dragged some distance before the driver stopped the car, and she died before medical assistance could be provided. This was in some ways a repetition of an earlier tragedy. In 1913 her two sons were killed in a motoring accident in Paris in a car in which they were returning home after lunch with their mother.

Harry Houdini (1874–1926)

The famed Hungarian illusionist was known for his impossible escapes, thanks in part to his extraordinary physical prowess. One night in October of 1926 some college students went to meet the magician after his show. One dared Houdini to let him punch him in the stomach to test his endurance and ability to withstand pain. Houdini agreed and unknowingly suffered a ruptured appendix. Despite intense pain he kept performing for a few days until he had to be rushed to a hospital. He died at dawn on October 31 from acute peritonitis.